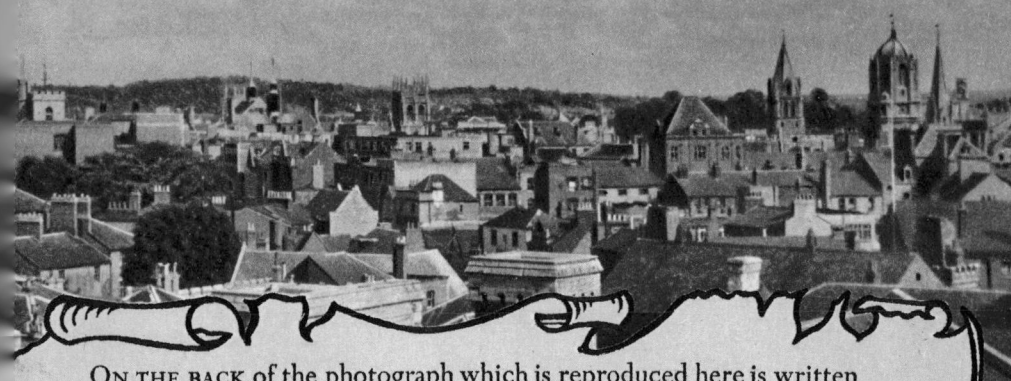

ON THE BACK of the photograph which is reproduced here is written in pencil: 'A View over Oxford from the Tower of St. Thomas's College.' tten below in another hand are the words: 'Surely not', followed by two tion marks. A careful survey from the summit of the Tower would no doubt de whether the photograph was in fact taken thence or from some other t of vantage. It is a curious fact that few members of Oxford Colleges well acquainted with the views from the Towers of their Colleges.

TO TEACH THE SENATORS WISDOM

OR

AN OXFORD GUIDE-BOOK

Books by J. C. MASTERMAN

AN OXFORD TRAGEDY (1933)
FATE CANNOT HARM ME (1935)
MARSHAL NEY, *A Play in Five Acts* (1937)

TO TEACH
THE SENATORS
WISDOM

OR

AN OXFORD
GUIDE-BOOK

BY

J. C. MASTERMAN

Provost of Worcester College, Oxford

LONDON

HODDER AND STOUGHTON

FIRST PUBLISHED JUNE 1952

REPRINTED 1953

MADE AND PRINTED IN GREAT BRITAIN FOR
HODDER AND STOUGHTON LTD., LONDON, BY
HAZELL, WATSON AND VINEY, LTD., AYLESBURY AND LONDON

*To the Fellows of Worcester College, Oxford,
in the hope that this book will afford them
some amusement and that they will extend to
the whims and idiosyncrasies of the Fellows
of St. Thomas's the same good-humoured toler-
ance which they have always shown to those of*

THE AUTHOR

ILLUSTRATIONS

facing page

Oxford in Wartime, from the painting by Paul Nash   87

In New College Chapel   114

"Alice's Shop", in St. Aldate's   127

The River in Eights Week, from the painting by Evelyn
Dunbar   133

Town and Gown, from the original sketch by the author of
Verdant Green   153

The Tutorial, from the painting by Edward I. Halliday   170

We pause for a reply, from the painting of a viva voce
examination by S. P. Hall   186

Undergraduate Conversation Piece, from the painting by
Edward I. Halliday   244

7

PROTECTIVE PREFACE

SOME years ago I wrote a work of fiction connected with the University of Oxford in which the characters were not drawn from life. Friends, however, are sometimes difficult to convince. "I liked your portraits of Oxford characters," said one of them to me, "and most of all the portrait of yourself." "Thank you very much," said I, but dared to ask no more—for the suspicion awoke in my mind that one character (whom I specially disliked) might be regarded as the self-portrait which I had unconsciously painted. Ever since I have longed, but feared, to know.

In this present book there is—to the best of my knowledge and belief—no portrait of any living person. If a 'gentle reader' was fashionable to-day, I should pray him (or her) to accept this statement without reservation; for among my acquaintances I do not number a Gresham or a Mitton, a Waterlow or a Prendergast. That individual traits of character of living persons have been used to build up my fictional characters is of course true, for how otherwise could any character come to life at all? But, I repeat, there is no complete picture, and even no caricature, of any living person. So much for that.

In the second place, I must make it clear that I do not subscribe to all—or indeed to many—of the views put forward by the Fellows of St. Thomas's. I might go further and say that some of their opinions shock me very much. If I sometimes shudder at their suggestions of reform I am more often appalled at the obstinate and complacent conservatism of the majority of them. Nor do I think that some of the doctrines and some of the heresies which they propound are answered and contradicted with half the power which might have been employed to discredit them.

9

Time after time I have longed myself to plunge into the argument —and have felt obliged to refrain. Even in some cases errors and inaccurate statements have been allowed to remain lest the course of the conversation should be interrupted.

Thirdly, I cannot vouch for the truth of all the stories narrated by the Fellows of St. Thomas's, and I strongly suspect that Tennant would have to stretch his conception of 'guide-book truth' widely to cover some of the anecdotes which he has admitted to the guide-book. At least no story is set down in malice. This sentence was confidently written, but doubt creeps in and caution warns. Let me say rather that I think, I believe, I hope that no story is inspired by malice, but I cannot be quite sure. (Does my notional 'gentle reader' murmur that the book would have been more readable had I been less cautious?) In any case I trust that no living person will feel hurt or aggrieved by any tale which has been included.

The perusal of the acknowledgments at the beginning of a book has often left me wondering whether, when all the acknowledged debts are taken into account, any substantial part of the book itself can be left to the credit of the author. With this thought in mind I shall content myself with recording a general expression of gratitude to many friends and many books, and confine my statement of specific obligation to a few persons only.

First, then, the illustrations. I am most grateful to Mr. J. R. H. Weaver, President of Trinity College, for three photographs, one of which is used for the end-papers of the book. The President must have gone to much trouble and inconvenience to take this photograph, for I am bound to assume that he ascended the tower of St. Thomas's to obtain it; Oxford men will need no reminding that that is an arduous climb. I am grateful, too, for leave to reproduce two pictures from the Junior Common Room at Worcester College—Paul Nash's *Oxford in Wartime* and Evelyn Dunbar's *The River in Eights Week*. The same courtesy has been accorded me by Mr. C. H. Wilkinson for his *Undergraduate Conversation Piece*, and by the Master and Fellows of Pembroke College for S. P. Hall's picture of the Viva (the Victorian title of which, *"We pause for a reply"* is worthy of the picture itself). Finally I am specially and deeply indebted to Mrs. Longden for permission to include *The Tutorial*.

For 'permission to quote' I must make acknowledgment and offer my thanks to the following authors and publishers: to Monsignor R. A. Knox and Messrs. Sheed and Ward for an extract from *Let Dons Delight*; to Dr. G. M. Trevelyan and Messrs. Longmans, Green & Co. for some sentences from the *English Social History*; to Mr. R. F. Harrod and Messrs. Macmillan & Co. for a passage from the *Life of John Maynard Keynes*; to Messrs. John Lane for an extract from Mr. Stephen Leacock's *Discovery of England*; to Sir John Murray for one from *Vice Versa*; and to the Oxford University Press for a quotation from the *New English Dictionary*. I am also indebted to Sir Ernest Barker for permission to make use of part of a letter of his written to *The Times*.

I am grateful—and not for the first time—to Mr. R. H. Dundas for reading my proofs; to Mr. I. G. Philip, Secretary of Bodley's Library, for kindly and generous help over one or two historical points and to the Warden of New College for similar assistance. To Mr. C. H. Wilkinson I owe a special debt; the traces of his influence will not, I think, remain unnoticed by those who know their Oxford at first-hand. His knowledge of the University, past and present, is profound; his knowledge of English Literature, both of this and of earlier times, is inexhaustible. No one with so rich a treasure in his keeping has ever been more prodigal in distributing it to others. Many a time I have hurried to his rooms to have a literary or historical question settled or an obscure reference found—seldom have I left without the appropriate answer. Often as I descend his stair with my conundrum solved, I recall the childhood tale of King Edward VII who, talking with an eminent scientist about a conjuring entertainment which he had watched with the fascinated eyes of a boy, remarked, "But Papa knows how *all* those things are done".

J. C. M.

*The numbers in brackets throughout the text
refer to the Notes at the end of the book.*

CHAPTER I

THE Fellows of St. Thomas's College in the University of Oxford have the reputation of doing themselves well—nor is the reputation wholly undeserved. Even at a time when rationing had cast its sombre shadows over the dinner tables of England and when six years of war had depleted the most capacious of the Oxford cellars, the common dinner of the Fellows still retained, as though by magic, much of its former distinction though it had perhaps sacrificed some of its amplitude and grandeur. In term time, it is true, the Fellows were wont to complain of the austerities forced upon them, and even ready, one and all, to assert—with an oath if need be—that their dinner was the precise counterpart of that served to the undergraduate members of the College in the body of the Hall. They believed this because the Bursar—good, easy man—had told them so, and it would have been clean contrary to the traditions of the College to have questioned a belief which gave them all a feeling of moral rectitude and patriotic self-abnegation. It was not in the spirit of the place to search out and expose unpleasant truths, and, indeed—as Tennant, the Curator of Common Room, was wont to point out—what sort of useful purpose could be served by convincing themselves that they ought to mortify the flesh more efficiently than they were compelled to do? "I quite agree," said Winn, always the defender of custom and tradition; "it is our duty, as it seems to me, to retain as much as we can of the graces and amenities of an age that has passed. Here in Oxford, if nowhere else, we should attempt to pass on something at least of what was best and most gracious in life as we knew it."

In term time the Fellows of St. Thomas's did themselves well;

in vacation they were apt to do themselves better. For then, and especially when only a few were dining, there seemed no valid reason why they should not enjoy themselves so far as the law would allow, or even a little further if no censorious eye was upon them. "The law," said the Chaplain, a little sententiously, "was made for man, not man for the law." "In considering breaches of the letter of the law, you must first consider whether there is anyone present remotely likely to take an objection," commented the Law Fellow. "In my view," said Winn, "the customs of the past should be preserved even at the risk of over-stepping the limits of rigid legality." "By which you mean," retorted the Bursar, who never forgot that he had been a soldier longer than he had been a don, "that with the sort of Government we get nowadays you are all damned glad if you can cheat it and take a bit more out of the kitty than anyone else." But the Bursar was a little sore—partly because the other members had failed to appreciate his latest method of serving lobster, partly because the order which compelled him to dine once a week with the undergraduates to demonstrate the excellence of the fare provided for them still rankled in his mind. (Why, thought Winn, does Trower always seem to me like an elderly bull in an arena looking round for matadors, and not quite happy if someone is not sticking banderillas into him? Or do I mean picadors—I never did know the difference). A polite shudder greeted the Bursar's rather brutal statement of the case, but no one seemed disposed to contradict his statement, for if there was one doctrine to which the Fellows of St. Thomas's subscribed more readily than to any other, it was the comfortable belief that the ignoring of unpleasant facts was the best method for getting rid of them.

No such unpleasant doubts, no faintest stirring of uneasy conscience, had troubled the eight men who had dined—reverently and at length—in the Common Room that night, for it was the middle of July, the dinner had been good, and the company, by chance rather than by design, select and satisfied with itself. Eight, thought Winn, as he glanced round the table, is surely the ideal number for a party of men—small enough for general conversation, large enough to sit silent without remark if one feels a little old, a little tired, a little inclined to relax without exertion. Small enough to create a feeling of solidarity and to maintain a community of views against the world; large enough for every shade of opinion to be voiced; large enough to man both sides in the hottest or in the flimsiest controversy. How much better than dinner in full term, when there may be twenty or thirty diners, half of them almost strangers to me. And what a lovely colour port is within the decanter, and how the silver gleams against the polished walnut. But is it walnut? I've asked the butler a dozen times, and I always forget the answer. I know the table was made from a tree which was felled in the President's garden in 1853— but was it a walnut? How strange it is that I remember some facts so clearly and forget others so easily. Or was it a foreign wood, and only the inlay came from the President's tree? I must ask Callender about it again—he's got a young mind and he always knows. (Callender was the butler and two years junior to Winn). Yes, surely, eight is the ideal number, especially when all of them harmonise with one another. For a moment the sense of complete well-being, the realisation of the harmony and beauty of life and of traditional ways, the belief in the fitness of things, gave Winn that satisfaction which he felt rarely and only in the Senior Common Room of St. Thomas's. (1) But, alas! only for a moment. How transient, after all, it all was! How changed the company since his early days—for how much longer would he himself sit in his accustomed chair?

> *And when Thyself with shining Foot shall pass*
> *Among the Guests Star-scatter'd on the Grass,*
> *And in thy joyous Errand reach the Spot*
> *Where I made one—turn down an empty Glass.*

Contentment among the old, he thought, is never far removed from nostalgia. It was a perfect summer night; they had dined well; the night air coming in through the open windows was balmy; the lighted candles cast a pool of light on the table in the centre of the room. But here in Oxford, the home of youth, were they not all ageing? How short life was—how brief enjoyment! How many of them at the table had been seated there twenty or even fifteen years back—how many would be seated there twenty years on? War and promotion and domestic upheavals had done their part. Always there seemed to be changes, and changes, whatever the Radicals might say, were always for the worse.

Unconsciously Winn cast an appraising eye at each of his colleagues in turn. He himself was by many years the senior. A scholar of the College, he had become in turn tutor in Modern History, Senior Tutor, and Vice-President. He had never known, and perhaps never desired, any other life or any other society. At 70 his teaching career had come to an end, but that was in wartime, and the College, which valued his devotion and liked him in spite of—or perhaps because of—his idiosyncrasies and his almost spinsterish prejudices—had refused to cast him adrift into a cold and alien world. Instead they had allowed him to retain his rooms and fellowship, and charged him with the task of writing the College history. Now he was 76, and though no day passed of which he did not spend some part in pursuing his investigations, it was becoming clearer and clearer to all but Winn himself that no publisher was ever likely to receive the manuscript of the completed history.

Four others at the table had spent the later part of the period between the wars at St. Thomas's. Trower, the Bursar, a retired soldier, who never forgot his earlier military life, was now 64, but he had, in fact, spent a couple of years as an undergraduate at St. Thomas's before he entered the Army. He still retained a kind of boyish heartiness and bluffness, which caused his friends to shrink and roused his enemies to exasperation. Mitton, the Chaplain, though in the early forties, was curiously untouched by four years as a Chaplain in the Forces, and had still the pink and cherubic complexion which Winn remembered fifteen years before. Nor had he lost anything of the *naïveté* of his earlier years. (Or do I mean not *naïveté* but a sort of commonplace approach, thought Winn. I always know what he will say about any topic —it's just what a Chaplain would say. No, it wasn't really a good appointment. No doubt Mitton is *au fond* a good man, but a College Chaplain ought to be intellectually the equal if not the superior of his colleagues—otherwise you get ribaldry). Winn sighed and turned his head to the next diner. David Prendergast, the Law Tutor, had changed little (let me see, Winn thought, what would he be? 54, 55—about that, I think) but perhaps he had become a shade cynical and disillusioned. His love of innovation and change, his support of experiment and his avowed belief in the unconventional, were now a little more than a habit of mind, almost an affectation. Can a lawyer really be a Radical? thought Winn. I doubt it. The precedents will be too much for him in the end, whatever he may say. But I wish Prendergast was a little less hard and a little less cocksure—and Winn sighed again. Robert Tennant, who sat next to Prendergast, was only a little younger (I know exactly, thought Winn, for I elected him to a scholarship in 1919 and he took the Schools in 1922—a good first it was, too. Well, if he was 18 in 1919, he's 48 now). A year or two abroad in the early twenties had been followed by a fellowship, which he had vacated for the duration of the war. He had returned to fill Winn's old place as senior History Tutor and was also Dean. He was, if anyone was, the live wire of the Senior Common Room—active, enterprising, intellectually alert, possibly a little dominating and self-assertive, but for all that friendly, able, versatile, and loquacious. The other three, though two of them were already middle-aged, had come only recently to St.

Thomas's. Gresham, who taught Classics, had spent two or three years as Professor in a Scottish University, but the lure of Oxford had been too strong for him and he had returned just before the war. Waterlow—the Hon. John Waterlow—had had more varied experiences; a couple of years as a lecturer at Christ Church, and a career of some distinction in the Diplomatic Service, had been followed by a military career of even greater distinction, in the course of which he had lost an arm. He had come, to St. Thomas's in 1945 to teach Modern Languages. In his case an inherited love of Oxford had drawn him irresistibly back again; his father, before coming rather unexpectedly into the family title, had been a don before him, and Waterlow himself had amassed a store of tales and traditions of an earlier Oxford not much, if at all, inferior to that of Winn himself. The last of the diners was Pacey, youthful, good-tempered, opinionated but not very articulate, and prickly as some scientists are. Winn, who was naturally charitable but certainly conventional in his tastes, always tried—with little success—to forget that Pacey had been educated at London and that he was a scientist. (Waterlow must be 50 at least, Gresham nearer 60, and I suppose Pacey is 27 or 28. Well, well, average age over 50. I suppose it's all right, but we *are* rather an elderly society. Ought there not to be more young men to teach the young? Can we really appreciate their point of view? Or do we even want to? Isn't this modern age too full of hurry and bustle and materialism? Don't we represent the best tradition of the Oxford of the past? Don't we stand for the maintenance of all that is best worth preserving? Don't we . . . ?)

A remark of Prendergast's brought Winn abruptly out of his reverie.

"In my opinion," said the Law Tutor, "all the suggestions so far are wrong. What we ought to have in this room is fluorescent lighting."

"I agree," said Pacey. "It's the most efficient form of lighting

18

now, and the medical people, on the whole, think it harms the eyes least."

Winn's thin cheeks flushed. "What utter folly," he said; "you really cannot think seriously of destroying the Common Room in that way. Let me tell you that when I came up to St. Thomas's for my scholarship examination in ninety-one (no, ninety), I was invited to dinner by old Fothergill in this very room. A great honour it was—I remember how nervous I felt and how kind everyone was—I remember how courteous the President was (that was Eccles, who was President, before Vereker). He treated me, a schoolboy, as though I were an equal—let me see, what was I saying? Oh yes. The candles were on the table, just as they are now; I thought that I had never seen a more beautiful room, and I never have. Fluorescent lighting! I don't know what fluorescent lighting is, but I dislike it—I dislike it very much indeed. I abominate it."

Prendergast laughed. "I can't understand you, Winn," he said. "You are the mildest of men. If I told you that the Bursar had absconded with the College cash, you would probably say that the poor fellow must be in very straitened circumstances, and you'd start a subscription fund on his behalf."

"And if I said," added Tennant, "that one of the undergraduates had committed murder or bigamy, you would certainly say that there must be mitigating circumstances, and alternatively that, being a St. Thomas's man, he was surely innocent."

"Yet," went on Prendergast, "you would consign anyone to the lowest hell who suggested the smallest change in any College custom. I believe you would gladly torture anyone who advocated a serious innovation in Common Room."

Winn's irritation never lasted.

"I'm truly sorry," he said, "if I spoke with too much heat. Of course the young men must have their day, and if you want changes they must come. But I was thinking how much we keep here of the gracious things of life, and how little is preserved in the world elsewhere of those things which we used to love and venerate. It's not only that these things will disappear if we don't guard them, but that they will simply be forgotten. I should like to think that even if the coming generation cannot enjoy all the good things that we have, they could still at least know about it all and understand some of the charm and beauty of the past. But no one yet has written down any account of, say, this room and our life here, and all that it has meant to some of us."

"We are hoping that your history of the College will do something to correct that," said Gresham gently. "How is it getting on?"

"Well, I work at it and I collect material, and in time I hope that it will not be unworthy of the College. But sometimes, well, I wonder if I can ever quite bring it all together." He stopped, a little embarrassed, and seemed to be searching for words to explain his difficulties. Tennant came to his assistance.

"I think I understand. Isn't it Acton, 'the great mute student', all over again? All the history of Liberty in his head and almost too much knowledge to put on paper. Perhaps it's the great fault of all us dons. We spend so much of our lives criticising the work of others that we can't bring ourselves to be creative. We're continually polishing and refining and altering what we have done, and the world gets nothing. But it's a pity. If we wait for perfection, nothing ever gets done in this imperfect world."

Winn smiled. "But I have published one or two things in my day, you know," he said. "Some articles in the reviews, and my short life of Hampden and a study of the battle of Edgehill."

"Which took five years to write and ten minutes to read," murmured Waterlow to himself. "God help the history, unless old Winn lives to be a hundred and fifty." Aloud he said to Tennant: "But why don't you publish more? There's no earthly reason why you should not, unless you are afraid of having to scrap

20

your lectures and write some new ones. What are you writing now? The answer, I conclude, is just nothing."

"Sloth, you know," added the Chaplain, as he absent-mindedly helped himself to his third glass of port, "was adjudged one of the seven deadly sins."

"As was gluttony," retorted Tennant with some asperity. "You are quite wrong, and I think that I have a complete answer to all your criticism open and implied. So far from being idle and unenterprising, I have this very day taken the unalterable decision to write a masterpiece—which incidentally has been long in my mind. I shall start to-night to write the introduction, as it were, to the great work itself—the preparatory foundation—and this I shall complete in a week. Furthermore, every one of you here will actively assist me in the work."

A quiet somnolence had settled on the Common Room, but Tennant's words roused them all, and for the first time the whole table was drawn into the discussion. Experience had taught them that the Dean was a hard task-master, and that any half-promises of help in any of his schemes would have to be redeemed in full.

"What in the name of goodness is this masterpiece?" asked Gresham.

"Whatever wild-cat scheme it is, you may count me out," said Trower with military bluntness. "I have work to do in vacation as well as term. Elaborate jokes aren't much in my line, anyhow."

"No, no," said Tennant. "This isn't a joke at all. It's a perfectly serious proposition, which, if you will bear with me, I shall explain to you. I mean to write—I shall write—a guide-book to Oxford."

"A guide-book?" said Prendergast. "You must be mad."

"Now, please, don't interrupt, and let me explain to you. Years ago I came to the conclusion that of all the books that I might write, a guide-book would give me the greatest satis-

faction. What other single work could give comparable satisfaction to a creative artist? A great landscape painter may perhaps
give permanence to some beautiful scene, but at the best he can
only, as it were, put on record a single and a small piece of beauty.
Or think of the historian. He labours to re-create a picture of past
times; he pursues the truth with unremitting industry; he aims at
impartiality and curbs his historical imagination. He may in
the end succeed in finding the words to make his history fix
itself in our minds. But the writer of the guide-book has everything. If he likes description, he can describe; if he sets store by
his own artistic taste, he can praise the things he loves and urge his
readers to study them; if he passes judgment on works of art or
on men, who is to gainsay him? I think, perhaps, that that is the
final and most satisfying quality. It's the sense of power. Just
think of the author of a new Baedeker volume conducting his
researches! He does not have to weigh the opinions of others or
cautiously compare the views of other men. Not for him the
timorous summings-up of the scientific historian. Instead, he
travels round with his pocket full of stars, which with princely
largesse he can scatter on this or that as he will. Every ancient
monument, every famous view, every natural beauty, every
great picture, every famous vintage, every hotel, every inn even
awaits his pleasure, suppliant for his praise. Do you remember
that speech of Nino Bixio's? 'I command here. I am everything.
I am Czar, Sultan, Pope . . . I must be obeyed like God.' That is
what the guide-book author is—when with royal gesture he
flings a second star, he is indeed a deity! Power! Everyone loves
power; to be a little god, however small the kingdom. Every
statement the guide-book writer makes is *ex cathedra*—un-
numbered thousands accept his word—all authority is his."

He paused and smiled at Waterlow.

"I remember, and you will too, the day that I decided that I
must write a guide-book, because we were together in Paris."

Waterlow laughed. "Yes, I think I know the story you are going to tell them—but carry on—it was an amusing experience."

"John and I were over on the Left Bank, and we found suddenly that it was rather late and we'd had no dinner, so we decided to drop into the first restaurant that looked promising. Let me see, we were somewhere in the area between the Odéon and the river, not far off the Boulevard St. Germain, the name of the street I can't remember. We soon found a restaurant—the usual thing, small, inviting, warm, a sort of atmosphere of culinary opulence within denying the modesty of the exterior. There were only half a dozen other people still at dinner, and I didn't pay much attention to them, but the waiter, who seemed to be *maître d'hôtel* and *sommelier* in one, impressed me at once. I remember that a look of pain, almost consternation, crossed his face when I began rather casually to order our dinner. 'But Monsieur cannot have that,' he exclaimed, 'he must not waste the chance that heaven sends.' It wasn't very long before that waiter had John and me in the hollow of his hand. I'm not quite sure now just what we ate—after all, I'm talking of twenty years ago—but I do remember that everything was superlatively, incredibly, uniquely good. I rather fancy (for I shut my eyes and the scene and the smells and the tastes come back to me) that we had a *pâté*, and a roast chicken and a cheese and a peach. I'm sure at least of the peach, for the waiter chose me one as though he had been selecting a candidate for Paradise. He had one of those big shallow boxes, and he seemed able to lift and appraise each peach so delicately and so gently that he did not even disturb its bloom. No ordinary fruit would suffice that night—but this at last, said he, this is the perfect peach—and so in my recollection it was. But if the food was good, what of the wine! I had entered the restaurant with the intention of drinking a *vin ordinaire*, and perhaps a *fine* with my coffee. But what chance was there of that? 'There is one wine here,' said the waiter, 'which you must drink. The patron lived in his youth in the Côte d'Or, all his relatives are there still, and there is a Burgundy here which . . .' Well, of course, we drank it; you remember that wine, John?"

"I do, indeed. It had that odd and veritable pig-dung flavour of the great Burgundies—a little heavy and vinous for my taste, but, my God! how good it was."

Tennant went on. "We drank two bottles of it, and the world grew rosier all the time. The restaurant had emptied by that time, and we and the waiter were left alone. I ordered coffee. 'And of course brandy', said the waiter. I hesitated, and really I thought he would have burst into tears. 'Listen, Monsieur,' he said, 'the patron has here a famous, an incomparable Armagnac; for the credit of the house you cannot, you must not, leave without tasting it.' The balloon glasses were on the table before I could find any answer, and then he brought one of those great ancient bottles which give the appearance of inexhaustibility. And he poured the precious liquid into our glasses—not a mere trickle but a great, generous portion. I suppose there was nearly half a pint of the Armagnac in each of our glasses. You, John, were just sober enough to remark that you supposed that we should have to pay the earth for all that mighty tipple."

"And you, Robert, said that in all the circumstances you didn't care a damn what we paid—if, indeed, it was as good as the Burgundy."

"And was it?"

"In all my life," said Waterlow, with simplicity and decision, "I have never drunk better, and I never shall."

"We savoured it, and later we smoked a little, and we talked a lot, and at long, long last I asked for the *addition*, and I must admit that I unfolded the little bit of paper with a sort of curiosity coupled with a reckless determination to pay anything however gigantic without the slightest question, for we had indeed dined like princes. (What a solemn moment that is! Somehow there's nothing in asking for the bill, but the words *l'addition, s'il vous plaît* seem almost a piece of religious ritual. You must time that simple sentence just at the exact moment. Now, you say, the evening has reached its end—all has been well. Had it ended earlier, pleasure would have been lost; had it lasted longer, the full flavour would have evaporated! Now is the moment, exactly timed). And then I looked and looked at the total, and I wondered if I was really too drunk to take it all in; because, you see, the bill for that meal for the two of us came to about five shillings, or some such ridiculous sum. I felt that the reputation for integrity of all British visitors was in my hands; I called for the waiter"— ("And made him a very long and flowery speech," interpolated Waterlow)—"and did nothing of the sort. I told him briefly but honestly that the wine and the brandy had been indeed superb, that he must have made a miscalculation, and that we must of course pay him properly. How, I said, could the patron possibly supply such nectar at such a price?"

"And the waiter smiled—a friendly, understanding, brotherly smile.

" 'Ah,' said he, 'but the patron committed the unpardonable blunder of giving me notice this morning.' "

"I walked out of that restaurant as though I owned all the world, and there and then I made my resolve to write a guide-book. I would go all over France, or at least all over Paris, and dine wherever fancy led me. And then, at the end of the meal, I would place one star or two stars or even three against the house where I had dined, and generations of travellers after me would follow my example and applaud my taste. But when once again I met that waiter, and when he had directed me through another meal, only then I should abandon every sort of caution and let a whole constellation of stars fall upon his restaurant."

"But you forget," said Trower, who was nothing if not practical, "the appalling boredom and the immense labour of collecting all the information about hotels and restaurants alone, and even that would only be a fraction of the work necessary for compiling your guide-book. Why, the detailed work would break you in no time."

"You may be an excellent Bursar, but you are not a poet," retorted Tennant. "That was only the spark which fired me, and of course I never intended to rival Baedeker in Paris or anywhere else. But I'm not sure that I've not started all this from the wrong end. Let me think a moment, and then I'll explain to you how the two plans came to be woven into one another."

He thought for a moment, and then went on but with a certain hesitation. "It was like this, I think. I always wanted to write about Oxford. You know, I loved the place, as we all have, from the moment that I first came here. And somehow that challenge of Quiller-Couch's always got under my skin:

> *Know you her secret none can utter?*
> *Hers of the Book, the tripled Crown?*

.   .   .   .   .   .

> *Know you the secret none discover?*
> *Tell it—when you go down.*

Why shouldn't that secret be discovered, and told? Why, at least, should not those who cannot come here, or only come for a brief visit, why should not they be told something of the secret of the place—something of its atmosphere and its beauty and its life? Why shouldn't they have their eyes opened to some of the things we've known here, and enjoyed? And again the answer seemed to me to be a guide-book."

Trower snorted his protest. "But that's been done hundreds of times—and, anyhow, you'd never have the patience or the knowledge to describe every college and tell its history. Besides——"

"Please, please, Bursar, don't interrupt me. Honestly you don't understand a bit what I mean. My Oxford guide-book isn't going to be like that in the least. A guide-book of the ordinary kind, full of facts and detailed descriptions and statistics and useful information—good heavens, what could be more awful! 'Guide-books are usually *biblia abiblia*, books that are not books but assemblies of facts strung together by innocent amateurs or sweated hacks.' I read that somewhere in a review the other day. But *my* guide-book isn't like that at all. Enough description of scenes and buildings to whet the appetite, enough description of representative men and types to make them live in the reader's mind; accounts of the lives men live here, the things they do, their thoughts, the books they read, the arguments they have one with another. It's not to be a book of reference; it's to be much more a work of the imagination. I want to make the reader see what Oxford really is. And, above all, the distinguishing characteristics of the work—omissions and digressions."

"What do you mean by that?" asked Prendergast.

"To begin with an Irishism, the book will be full of omissions. If you go to a cathedral with Baedeker, you will be told how many chapels there are on the south side of the nave and how many on the north, and what is in each of them. But all I want is the illustrative fact, not the complete list, still less the catalogue. I believe that one could write a good guide-book to Oxford with, say, no mention of New College or Christ Church. You see what I mean?"

"Yes, I think so; but what about the digressions? Why are they so important?"

"They're more than important, they're the essence of the whole thing. After all, the best guide is the enlightened and instructed friend, the man with whom you can discuss the ideas that lie behind what you are seeing, and the controversies and discussions which spring from those ideas. Suppose I took you to the Examination Schools—and the guide-book will take you there, no doubt—I shouldn't tell you that they were opened in 1882, though I think they were. I might tell you that they cost £100,000, as I believe they did, but that would only be to start a talk about the relative value of money then and now, and to discuss whether buildings were ever a really good investment. Quite certainly we should very soon be arguing hotly about the merit of competitive examinations in choosing the best men; obviously we should get equally heated about the value of the viva, and probably competing to be the first to describe Gladstone's viva in his schools. And from that I suppose that we might reasonably expect to go on to analyse Gladstone's career and character, and from that we should——"

"Enough, enough," said Prendergast, "you make your point. I'm satisfied that digressions will form the major part of the book. It does seem to me, though, that you'll find it difficult to adapt your literary style to an undertaking which is to include descriptions of scenes and places, and, as I understand it, imaginative reconstructions of the lives of past Oxonians, together with historical and philosophical arguments on every subject under the sun."

"I've thought a lot about the style," admitted Tennant, "and I admit that it presents difficulties. For the body of the work I've got to risk being dogmatic; for, after all, dogmatism is the price we pay for brevity. I fancy that Macaulay's cocksureness is the model for the guide-book writer, at least up to the point where he begins to digress——"

"Let me recommend Defoe as your model," said Waterlow. "You'll remember that he could lie like truth."

"Isn't the modern idiom rather that of Neville Cardus or Robertson-Glasgow?" suggested Prendergast. "I mean to say, when they're describing a cricket match they make you feel all the human issues which lie behind it."

"Exactly," said Tennant. "I entirely agree. That's the journa-

28

list's art in its highest form, though I think Harold Nicolson or Peter Fleming would have come first to my mind as the master of that style I aim at. And then the quotations. I always feel that aptly chosen quotations are the salt of any book; yet the author dare not use them too much. The guide-book could and should. Where I do find difficulty is in thinking how to treat of persons. You can build up a living picture of a man if you have a whole chapter to play with, but how do you make him live in a couple of sentences? Sometimes, of course, the right words come, and you feel that the true verdict has been given once and for all. I suppose that's what Gresham would call the lapidary merit of Latin."

Quite unexpectedly old Winn plunged into the discussion. "I remember," he said, "when I was a young man, staying at a seaside hotel on the French coast. One of the great Oxford men of learning, a lawyer and legal historian, was residing temporarily at another hotel about two miles away, and he flattered me by asking me to call on him. I used, in fact, to visit him quite often. I won't tell you his name, but it was a household word then. He was old and deaf, and nearly blind and very rheumatic, but excellent company all the same. His brother was staying with him—he was less distinguished, but even more fragile and much more decayed in his faculties as well as in his physical condition. (Don't get impatient, Mitton, I am coming to the point, and I shall forget it if you hurry me.) Oh yes, I remember. I went out one day from the hotel, a lovely day it was too, in order to take a bathe in the sea. I think sea-bathing is a healthy practice in early and middle life, though I fancy that it should not be indulged in too often. Now where was I—oh yes—when I came back in the late afternoon my hotel-keeper said to me, 'Monsieur D. called on you when you were out'. Now that was a great honour, for it meant that an old gentleman had walked a long way on a hot day to see a very undistinguished young man. I was pleased, very pleased, but then quite suddenly I realised that I didn't know *which* Mr. D. had called on me. It was a great predicament."

"Whatever did you do?" asked Mitton, with the faintest touch of sarcasm.

"I thought out the problem, and I finally decided to ask the hotel-keeper. I said to him was it Mr. D. or his brother that called on me? Both of them, as I should have told you, were well known in those parts. The hotel-keeper thought for a time, and then he replied, '*Le moins affligé*'. Then I knew at once. Now you see the point of my story. You mustn't trust to your own power of description to hit off a man; you must try to see him through the eyes of someone who can judge him fairly and from a viewpoint better than yours. And don't be afraid of quotation (though I quote too frequently); if a thing is once said well, why try to say it otherwise? All the best writing is built up on quotations."

"Excellent, Winn, and true," commented Prendergast. "And who will give us the best and truest picture of the undergraduate —either the undergraduate of to-day or of yesterday?"

"His scout, or the College porter, or the butler," replied Waterlow without hesitation. "I remember one undergraduate who was sent down after a very short but lurid career of one term, in the course of which he spent about two years' income, mainly on drink from the buttery. I asked the College butler what he thought of him. 'A somewhat free batteler, Sir', was the answer. I thought that was charitable as well as true. And then I'm reminded of another case. There was a man, so my old father told me, who came up only for a year before the 1914 war; he was killed in 1915 or 1916, and given a posthumous V.C. The trouble was that when the College record came to be written no one could remember anything about him. Finally someone thought of asking his scout, and the scout gave his verdict. 'He was the nicest gentleman, Sir, that God ever put on a staircase!' That's Winn's point over again; we may think of an undergraduate as the man who comes to us for a tutorial, or the man who rows in the College eight; but the scout thinks of him as the man God puts on his staircase. And that is surely the better view-point."

"In my opinion," said Trower, "the clearest descriptions are generally those you get in the Army or from the police. They tell you what a man looks like, and you can usually guess his character pretty accurately from the cut of his jib. I remember, though, in the war that I got hold of one of your fancy descriptions and found it useful. I was dealing with M.I. in London, and they wanted to trace some fellow of an Oxford College who had been seen at some meeting or other. He wasn't suspected of anything subversive or anything of that sort, but they thought he might be able to give them some information about the meeting. The only snag was that they didn't know his name, so they sent a Special Branch man to describe him to me. I expected the usual thing— height five foot eleven, weight round about 160 pounds, thick fair hair brushed back, dark-grey suit and all the rest of it—but I got nothing of the sort. My policeman, who I'm bound to say seemed to me rather a modern la-di-da sort of chap, thought a bit and then said 'He looked to me like a swimming-bath attendant'."

"And you knew who it was?" enquired Pacey, whose scientific interest was aroused.

"Of course I did, but you won't. He was not, I need hardly say, a fellow of St. Thomas's."

"The truth, I see," said Tennant, "is that the best descriptions are so often—perhaps because they come straight from the heart, or do I mean the shoulder?—so often couched in the vernacular, and not even grammatical. There's a widespread misapprehension that men of action cannot use words, and yet at need they can always, it seems to me, get across just what they wish. I'm not thinking of Napoleon, for he was a true master of language for the occasion, but think of Oliver Cromwell and read his letters and speeches. He couldn't easily compose a grammatical sentence, but still he makes his meaning as clear as crystal and convinces you at the same time."

Winn made another unexpected contribution to the discussion.

"Years ago," he said, "I went to Berkeley Castle, and was shown a horrible iron instrument with which, it was alleged, Edward II had been done to death. I do not myself believe in the authenticity of this instrument; but that is neither here nor there. When the guide showed it to me he said, 'If you know what the poor old king was done to, this is what he was done it to with'. That was not grammatical, but it seemed to me to be a terse and vivid description."

"I hear the child's complaint," said Mitton, "'Oh Mother, whatever did you choose that book for me to be read to out of for'. Grammar won't help you, Tennant."

"It won't, indeed; but then a Fellow of St. Thomas's cannot be ungrammatical—at least not consistently. I comfort myself, though, with that devastating analysis which George Moore makes of the style of Thomas Hardy."

"My own feeling," said Prendergast, "is that by far the best model is Abraham Lincoln. Let me remind you of some of his descriptions and stories."

"The mention of stories," said Tennant, "suggests another merit in the guide-book. In most books a story to be interesting has to be new, but it's the very essence of the guide-book that it should contain the good chestnuts. Most Oxford stories have been told a hundred times in twenty different Common Rooms. The guide-book should be the chestnuts' Valhalla. The majority of people like chestnuts, just as they like to read of things they know by personal experience. Haven't you ever thought how much more exciting a book like, say, Cobbett's *Rural Rides* or *Lavengro* is than Marco Polo or Hakluyt? Why is that? Simply because you know the scenes and recognise the places. The Oxford guide-book should start with the most aged of Oxford chestnuts."

"And what is that?" asked Mitton.

"Naturally the story of the Oxford gardener. The American visitors admire his lawn. 'How is it possible to get this perfect surface?' 'Quite easy. You mow and roll and cut and roll, and you go on doing that for two or three hundred years, and there is your lawn.' Of course the facts are wholly otherwise, for most of the Oxford gardens date back only to the nineteenth and some only to the early twentieth century. Still, the story is a good one, for it gives the sense of continuity as well as any story I know. Think, too, how the guide-book is proof against criticism. You write an article for the *Oxford Magazine* and everybody sniffs and murmurs 'sententious'—but a guide-book should be sententious and can count that as a sign of merit."

Gresham, though he had not spoken, had followed the argument with due attention. He now, with a deprecating smile, himself intervened.

"Are we not allowing ourselves to be diverted from the purpose of our conversation?" he enquired. "I realise that the guide-book is to be a starting-point, as it were, for an exposition of Tennant's views on a great variety of subjects, and that the digressions are to be, indeed, the main content of the book—but we are not writing this guide-book; we are only listening to Tennant's exposition of his plan, and from that we have been diverted by the agreeable anecdotes and reminiscences of Winn and you others. I suppose that all of us thought half an hour ago that Tennant was only playing gracefully and fancifully with the pretty conceit of his guide-book, but well . . . I confess that I myself am nervous."

T.S.W.—3

"What the devil do you mean by that?" grunted Trower. Gresham smiled again.

"Precisely what I say, Bursar. You will recollect Disraeli's remark about Bismarck—'Take care of that man, he means what he says'. Now, I have the uneasy conviction not only that Tennant intends to write his guide-book, but also that he intends to place us under contribution. Why should he take all this trouble to commend his scheme to us unless he proposes that we should come to his assistance? *Timeo Danaos et dona ferentes*, O my dear Tennant—that is the reason for my nervousness. Do I not detect the possibility of a Long Vacation spoiled for some of us? If you have your wicked way, do I not see the more malleable among us acting as your literary assistants instead of enjoying our well-earned leisure? No doubt we shall succumb; but pray be honest and answer me two questions. Failing a sufficient answer, I shall inaugurate what is called, I believe, a sit-down strike."

"*Touché*—ask your questions by all means."

"The first is this. You have the laudable ambition of writing a guide-book which shall both describe the best things in Oxford, and also convey something of Oxford's secret to your readers. Now surely that is a subjective matter. Why, then, do you seek to make your colleagues participate in what should be a purely personal enterprise? My second question is similar to the first. You have long had this project in mind; why, then, this sudden urgency, this abrupt change from thought to action?"

Tennant thought for a moment or two before he made his reply.

"I think," he said, "that I will answer your second question first. You are wholly right in supposing that my book is a serious proposition. From time to time during the last twenty years I have thought of it—now and then I have jotted down a note or an anecdote which seemed to me worthy of inclusion—but always it has been a distant prospect beckoning me on but always

34

hazy in the future. I think that is how things do happen. We dream our dreams and build our airy castles—and often enough that is all—but sometimes something occurs which changes phantasy into reality. The pure mathematician, Pacey, loses all his cherished purity and becomes an applied mathematician.'

"No, no," protested Pacey, "no two habits of mind could be more alien to one another than those of the pure and the applied mathematician."

"Never mind, I've chosen my illustration badly, but you must see what I'm driving at. Suddenly, as in this case, a long-cherished and imaginary—or do I mean imaginative—project suddenly becomes a practical and urgent task. The hour strikes, the man is ready, there is a sort of inevitability about the whole event."

He paused again and looked round the table.

"I do not think I need ask anyone here," he said with a smile which was almost a grin, "if he is acquainted with Sir John Boomer, ninth baronet of——"

"My God," ejaculated Prendergast, "don't say that he is going to pay us a visit."

"Calm yourself, he is, in fact, leaving for South Africa this week, or so he tells me in a letter which reached me this morning."

A sigh of relief seemed to come from every one of those sitting at the table.

Sir John Boomer was, in his own estimation at least, by far the most distinguished of the old members of St. Thomas's. The head and only surviving member of an old county family, which for many generations had sent its members to the College, he was also the possessor of great wealth, acquired by his eighteenth-century forebears in India. Himself a bachelor, he had thrown himself in early life into every kind of public work, provided only that he was assured of adequate publicity. No new Imperial or Colonial League or Society, no organisation for the improvement of international relations, no great charitable appeal, could be considered worthy of support unless Sir John was among its sponsors. In his own Midland county it would have appeared as something contrary to nature if a meeting had been held at which he had not taken the chair; a great school or a hospital in the district which had failed to secure him on its board of governors might be said to have marked itself for gradual but inevitable failure and decay; he had made more public speeches (or, as his detractors put it, had made the same speech more often) than any man in the country, no politician barred, and had derived more pleasure from making them than anyone in the world. Amongst all these activities, however, he always found time to busy himself with the varied activities of his old College, of which he was an Honorary Fellow. No doubt the Fellows had not been altogether neglectful of the possibility of future benefits when they had elected him, but bitterly had some of them regretted what had seemed—at the time—a politic act. For he had arrogated to himself the function of head alumnus and tutelary deity. Hardly a term passed in which he did not visit St. Thomas's, and on every occasion he took it on himself to lecture the President, to address the undergraduates, to instruct the Fellows about their duties, and to suggest (or sometimes to dictate) reforms and improvements in the management of College affairs. There was no Fellow who did not regard him as a menace, but the thought of the million or millions which he might be expected to leave to the College drove all criticism below ground. How could such a bequest be thrown away by unworthy impatience or personal antipathy? That, at least, was the view of Winn, who had suffered longer and more acutely than the rest. "The worst of Boomer is," he had said once, "that he is essentially a vulgarian. I cannot imagine why, considering his breeding and upbringing, he should be both quite so vulgar and so lacking in taste and sensibility. If he were humourless, it would be more bearable, but unfortunately he has a sort of perverted sense of humour—he likes practical jokes, for example—and that all makes it worse. Still, we must consider the interests of the College and remember that he will be our greatest benefactor, and we ought to disguise our own feelings about him." Even Vereker, who had been President between the two wars, and who had never been known to say an uncharitable thing about any man, had been stirred out of his accustomed calm by a visit from Boomer.

"I am vexed to think," he had said at the end of a long and unusually irritating evening spent in Common Room, "that that man is regarded in many quarters as peculiarly a person of whom this College should be proud."

"Ah," said Winn, "we must be charitable and remember that he is to be a great benefactor."

"I am tempted to remember also," retorted the old President with unusual acerbity, "that benefactors are of little value until they are dead."

"But if the great Sir John is not going to honour us this month, for what conceivable reason have you disturbed our peace by introducing his name into this very select company?" asked Prendergast.

Tennant laughed. "I'll read you his letter," he replied, drawing from his pocket a large and impressive sheet of notepaper. "This is what he says:

" 'My dear Tennant,
    'A mutual acquaintance ["He means common," murmured Gresham] has informed me that you intend to spend the month of July in Oxford. At any time of the year no more congenial milieu could be found than our old College, and in

37

this instance I am especially delighted to know that you are in residence, for you will be able to do both me and the College itself a service—without undue inconvenience to your good self.

'Let me tell you in the fewest possible words what this service is. You will recollect that towards the end of the war I undertook a mission for H.M.G. to the United States. ["Will he ever let us forget it," murmured Prendergast.] I think that I may say that my mission had some small effect in bringing the great struggle to its triumphant conclusion, but I venture to think also that its indirect effects in cementing the bonds of unity and friendship between us and our great transatlantic allies ["He would call them that," from Waterlow] far transcend even the not inconsiderable immediate results. Many times in my speeches and Press conferences I stressed the often forgotten truth that increased knowledge of each other's way of life and of each other's problems and difficulties would infallibly bring both nations more closely together in friendly and wholehearted co-operation and to the manifest benefit of us both and indeed of the whole world. ["*Must* you read it all?" Waterlow questioned. "I'm not sure if I can bear the whole speech."] But enough of that. ["Thank God," from Prendergast.] During my period of service at Washington I made many friends. [They only let him stay a month, didn't they? Three weeks, I think.] And it so happens that some of these friends are now visiting this country. To three of them in particular I owe a debt which I can now repay.

'They are allotting a few days to Oxford, a time which, as I have impressed upon them, is all too short, and I have accordingly reserved rooms for them at the Mitre from Wednesday, the 20th, to the following Saturday.' "

(A sigh of relief came from Winn, Trower, and Waterlow

simultaneously. Each one of them had been expecting that the College would be called upon to house and entertain the guests).

" 'It is perhaps hardly necessary for me to say that I had originally proposed to give myself the pleasure of acting as their cicerone, but duty is a peremptory task-master whom I for one cannot disobey. My passage to the Cape is booked for to-morrow, and I cannot postpone a mission which may prove to be of some delicacy and, I trust, of some service to the State. So, my dear Tennant, I bethought myself of you, and of the ancient traditions of hospitality for which St. Thomas's has always been distinguished. I feel assured that you will find it a source of pride and gratitude to act as a guide in Oxford to these friends of mine, and I have taken it upon myself to instruct them to wait upon you about noon on the Wednesday. You will, therefore, have no trouble at all in making arrangements to contact them. It ought, I think, to be possible for you to show them many at least of the beauties of our dear Alma Mater in the three days at their disposal. You will remember that these folk have been friends both to me and to the Allied Cause ["He was always strong on priorities," murmured Waterlow] and will treat them, I have no shadow of doubt, with that in your mind.' "

(So far the letter had been typed—the rest was in the sprawling but majestic hand of the Baronet).

" 'The College, I trust, is prospering. I must confess, though, that I have been in some measure perturbed during this last six months, for I have seldom seen St. Thomas's names in the public Press, and I was disappointed to observe that the eight sank from third to fifth place in the summer eights. We must not relax our efforts in any sphere. I do not like to see more Balliol than St. Thomas's men entering the public services. Are we staffed quite as well as we should be? Pacey, no doubt, is a worthy young man [This is where you bow, Pacey!], but I sometimes wonder whether we do not need some scientist of European reputation. Trower, I know, is a thoroughly good fellow [That's something for your obituary, Bursar!], but again I am a little dubious whether he is entirely *au fait* with all the advances which we have made in administration and in problems connected with catering and housing. You might, I think, stimulate him gently and introduce some innovations and improvements with all your well-known tact. He should not be allowed to lag too far behind the times. I think that many of you tend to forget that in these days Oxford can no longer remain the secluded monastery, where scholars and priests are segregated from the world, as it was in the past. You must move with the times and keep pace with progress. I should like to feel sure that the College guests-rooms will be renovated and fitted with such modern amenities as science has put within the reach of us all before I pay you my next visit in the autumn. Commend me to Winn. I thought him failing a little—in mind, I mean, rather than in body—when last I came to the College, but he is a loyal and devoted member of our society, and it would pain me to think that his declining years were darkened by any criticism, however well justified, of his competence. I think that he would be naturally gratified if you were to ask him to show my friends round St. Thomas's; after all, he knows the College as well as any man alive, and they perhaps would gain something from conversing with an old scholar of bygone days.

'Pray do not give yourself the trouble of acknowledging this letter, for I shall have sailed by the time it reaches you. I am glad to think that everything is happily arranged and that the whole organisation is in your capable hands.

> 'Yours very sincerely,
>
> 'John Boomer.

'P.S.—You may wish me to address the Junior Common Room after I return on my South African experiences, and, however hard pressed I am, I will make time to do so. I do not think that the Appointments Committee puts these overseas jobs with sufficient *empressement* before the young men. We must change all that.' "

"Could any man be more endearing?" asked Prendergast. "But are there no blessings for the rest of us? Why should Pacey and Trower and Winn alone receive their terminal reports? What about Mitton and John and myself? And even you, Robert, don't get a mention."

"He does," snapped Trower, "he's told in words of one syllable that he is the sucker of this party."

"What are you going to do?" asked Mitton. "It is provoking, no doubt, but I hardly see how you can refuse to help—for one thing Boomer is out of reach, and you don't even know the names or addresses of his friends. I suppose it is a Christian duty to assist if you can."

"Speaking as an honorary pagan *pro hac vice*," suggested Waterlow, "I should sport my oak, pin a notice on it saying 'gone away to Scotland for a month', and lie doggo till the danger is overpast."

"And face your merited punishment in the autumn—that's only to postpone the evil day," commented Winn. "That would be pusillanimous and unrewarding. I think you will feel compelled to assist in some measure in the entertainment of Sir John's guests. After all, the reputation of the College is to some extent involved. The chief difficulty, in my view, is that you know nothing at all about them."

"But we do. Has not Boomer declared that they enjoy the distinction of being friends both of the Allied cause and of himself? And what would three American friends of his be? Certainly not unpretentious men of learning or culture. Certainly not men of unrecognised talent or hidden virtue. No, no. They will be men whose names are well-known to the public Press of one continent at least. I have no doubt they will be all Senators, and that one at least will have immense journalistic influence."

"I don't think Boomer would be so unenterprising," objected Mitton. "My guess is that one will be a great business magnate, and one a Governor, and the third—well, probably a Judge or an Admiral."

"We must remember which American party is in power," said Winn a little acidly. "or we shall offend them. We can be confident that Boomer's friends will belong to the dominant party, whichever that may be; I always forget."

"Three eminent Democrats, then," said Tennant; "their exact titles to be settled later, though I stick to my Senators. Of course they will be Senators."

Gresham had been silent for some time, but as usual he had been following the conversation closely. He now intervened once more.

"This habit of digression, which Tennant affects so greatly to applaud, has once more, as it seems to me, led us astray. Am I not right in asserting that when we started to tear in pieces the character of Sir J. B., Tennant was in process of replying to the second of two questions posed by myself?"

"Yes," said Tennant, "I felt sure that you would come back to the point. Your second question was this: 'Why, when I had long toyed with the project of writing my guide-book, did

I suddenly decide to take action?' That was roughly it, wasn't it?"

"Precisely—and the answer?"

"You've guessed the answer already. My beautiful book, my perfect guide-book, would in normal circumstances never have been written, or at any rate never completed. I saw it as a great leisured book, straying into every inviting Oxford byway, building up gradually a great composite picture of Oxford and Oxford life. But now suddenly I am faced with a crisis. I have to 'put over' Oxford in three days to three American Senators (very well, three important American personages, if you prefer), and I am given a week to prepare myself. The answer comes like a flash. I will write a first instalment of my guide-book and present it to them. There they will find the answers to all their questions. They will return to the States believing that Oxford is the finest city in the world and that I am its greatest citizen; you will all realise that you have a genius in your midst, and Sir John Boomer, hearing the extravagant eulogies of the Senators, will have a stroke due to excess of emotion and will expire leaving his millions to the College."

"Then your precious guide-book will only be a little twopenny-halfpenny primer, after all," objected Trower.

"No, no. It will be nothing of the sort. I still cling to my original idea. It will be, as it was always to have been, a leisured book, built on omissions and digressions. The only change is that the omissions will be increased and the selection of illustrations restricted. Of course I know what questions an American visitor will ask, and these questions will be answered; but they'll be used to lead on to the digressions and to the things I mean to say. Besides, I shall keep the guide-book to myself—like the crib which the schoolmaster has concealed inside his desk. I shall use it throughout the three days, and when the Senators (yes, I must insist that they are Senators) leave, I shall in a nonchalant manner hand them each a copy. Here, I shall say, is a small thing of my own, a parergon of course, which will give you some idea of the true Oxford. It is written in preparation for a greater work on the same subject."

Gresham nodded in understanding. "And now," he said, "may I plead for an equally candid answer to my first question? The guide-book, as I remarked, is your account of Oxford; why do you propose to lay your patient colleagues under contribution whilst you are writing it? Or, if I may speak bluntly, why do you contemplate wrecking our peace and leisure as well as your own?"

"That question deserves, and will receive, a careful answer. If I had been able to carry out my original intention, there would have been no need of any such co-operation. I should have remained the 'chield amang you taking notes', gradually absorbing from your conversation the views and anecdotes which I required. But a hasty compilation such as I now have in mind demands different treatment. It will be my book, and I shall write it, but I must have the incentive—and not only the incentive but the constant, or rather the recurring, stimulus. No one can sit down and describe such things and men and ideas as I shall describe unless he has some such assistance. Everyone needs to have the best called out of him. Boswell isn't just the biographer of Johnson, or the narrator of his hero's life and wisdom. He evokes the epigram or the phrase: ' "That showed great fortitude of mind," says Boswell. "No, sir, stark insensibility," replies the sage.' And what about Sherlock Holmes—is he not inconceivable without Watson? Or Poirot without Hastings? Of course I must have my Watson if I am to display my full powers. Besides, are we not, at the very start, touching on part of the secret of Oxford? People may say that the University owes everything to the College system, and think they mean that living in Colleges is the *summum bonum* of University life, but, in fact, is not the tutorial system much more important? The College tutor doesn't pump in-

formation into his pupils (at least I trust the younger ones don't).
No, it's the weekly talk and discussion between pupil and tutor
which is the essence of Oxford life. If John Boomer had an hour's
refresher talk on Aristotle with Gresham each time he visited us
instead of talking for two hours himself on the Civil Service in
West Africa, he'd be a better and a wiser man, the undergraduates
would be happier, and West Africa would not materially suffer.
It's really the tutorial system I'm thinking of. It was said of
Bismarck, *Er Bedürfte immer der Reibung*. With me it is the
same. I need a Watson and a Hastings and a whole team of
Boswells. And I need them urgently, because my time is so short."

"And how exactly do we all fit in?" enquired Mitton.

"Well," said Tennant with a smile, "I don't exactly see a part
for Father Brown, if that is what you're thinking of."

"But the Bursar might perhaps double the two soldierly parts
of Watson and Hastings," hazarded Prendergast, not without
malice.

Trower was, perhaps fortunately, unacquainted with the
character of Hastings, but he expressed no approval of the
suggestion that he should fill the rôle of Watson.

"Gresham I see as a sort of Greek chorus," went on Tennant,
"drawing attention to the perils in our path. The rest of you, I
think, might form a kind of team of Boswells, pandering to my
weaknesses and exciting my critical qualities."

Gresham made one more effort to escape the toils which were
closing on the Common Room.

"Granted all your premises," he said, "and agreeing that you
are facing your problem with vigour and ingenuity, I am still
wondering why we should be expected to sacrifice the best week
of the summer to make ourselves the playthings of your fancy.
After all, Boomer wrote to you, and it is for you to satisfy him.
Why do you assume—if I may be allowed yet another question—
that we shall rally to your support? Surely our reasonable course

is to play the part, not of Boswell or Watson, but of the Levite who passed by on the other side ?"

"I expected that objection," Tennant replied, "and I can give you the answer. Each of you will help me for a different reason. Winn will think that the interests of the College will suffer if our benefactor is not placated; besides, he will be on tenterhooks lest any guide-book of Oxford should give insufficient space to St. Thomas's. David Prendergast will help because his intellectual interest is aroused; he does not believe that a book (even if it is only a crib for ourselves) can be written in a week, but, as he's saying to himself, there's no evidence, and he wants evidence because he always does. He is hoping that my optimistic forecast will not be fulfilled. Mitton is by nature bone-idle (now don't interrupt me, Mitton), but he cannot in decency refuse the appeal to his Christian principles—this is a work of friendly collaboration and he cannot resist the call of duty. John Waterlow will find it easier to say 'Yes' than 'No' partly because of *noblesse oblige*, partly because he could not bear the appearance of a guide-book which ignored all his best Oxford stories. Gresham will help because he loves Oxford and loves to talk of it. Pacey will help because he's a genuine scientist with the scientific spirit hot within him. No, I don't mean that—the cold, passionless man of science. He'd like to anlayse the secret of Oxford and tabulate his results; he likes to be able to show that $1\cdot1$ per cent. more useful inventions have been made at Oxford per square mile than in any other place. He looks on our plan as a scientific enquiry into Oxford, and he doesn't mean to be left out of it. Isn't that right—and right in every case ?"

"And what about me ?" said Trower in a somewhat aggrieved tone.

"My dear Bursar, how outrageous of me! Really I had taken your assistance as a matter of course, for how could any project in St. Thomas's prosper without you ? But since you ask, I must tell you why you will help. You will help in the first place because, in spite of some minor blemishes of character, you are fundamentally a good-natured man. In the second place you will help because, if I may use your own language, you'll be damned before you see a parcel of incompetent intellectuals make a mess of a piece of work which could be efficiently controlled by any one person of average horse sense. At this very moment, my dear Bursar, it is on the tip of your tongue to explain that you will bring your dictaphone into Common Room for the next week, that your efficient secretary will read off the records and type copies for us all by noon on the next day, and that corrected copies of the evening's work will be issued to all concerned by 22.00 hours on the following day. In short, you will not only help but you will take control of the entire undertaking. I myself shall assist the whole team by transferring my collection of Oxford books to the Common Room shelves so that quotations can be rapidly verified. Have I said enough?"

"Enough!!" said Prendergast.

"Too much," said Trower, though without conviction.

Gresham summed up the general feeling.

"My dear Dean," he said, "it is an old and sound principle that when a surrender has to be made, it should be made gracefully. How can we resist you? One man who knows what he wants is always a match for a dozen who know only that they want the maximum of peace and quiet. I see very well that we shall co-operate whether we wish to or not, so I for one will promise my support."

The Common Room had emptied and only Tennant and Winn were left.

"Well," said Tennant, "I've got my team, but I feel that virtue has gone out of me."

"You may have got your team, but you haven't got your

47

book," retorted Winn, gently wiping his pince-nez with a silk handkerchief. "And, frankly, I don't feel very much confidence in your team."

"How so?" asked Tennant.

"I was thinking earlier in the evening," said Winn, "that we were a society of elderly men, and as the discussion went on I felt more and more that we are all extraordinarily alike. You can't get a picture of Oxford from one angle only. I know that you will tell me that Prendergast is a lawyer and Mitton a parson and Pacey a scientist, but, really, they all think the same."

"I don't agree in the least," retorted Tennant. "In the first place, I believe that the permanent values in Oxford are independent of the views of individuals; secondly, I never intended, as Dr. Johnson would have put it, to let the Whig dogs have the better of it; and thirdly you're all wrong in saying that we all have the same point of view. Gresham was a rabid Asquithian Liberal when I first knew him; Mitton used to call himself a Christian Socialist, though I never knew what he meant; Prendergast is always in opposition to what party is in power because he thinks the Government is always incompetent; John Waterlow never belonged to any party, he's always been an intellectual; and Pacey, as you know, is an out-and-out Labour man who thinks that Socialism is the cure for every ill. You and Trower and I are the only true-blue Conservatives."

"You've missed the point, I fear," replied Winn a little testily. "Party politics have nothing to do with it. Don't you realise that everyone who stays here becomes inevitably a supporter of order and tradition—in so far, that is, as Oxford is concerned. The wildest and most red of all our Socialists are always the supporters of College tradition and Oxford habits. Whatever they are in politics or in the world, they are Conservatives here. Why, we even speak alike. Trower may allow himself a few military expressions, and John Waterlow retains something of the precious style of the Foreign Office, and of course Pacey hasn't absorbed the spirit of the place yet; but in the main we all live and think and speak alike. The spirit of the place is too strong for us. Perhaps that is something to start your guide-book with. The strength of tradition." He gently blew out the last of the candles. "Fluorescent lighting—what an abomination," he murmured to himself.

CHAPTER II

"How do we begin?" enquired Prendergast.

"The beginning, to my mind," said Mitton, "is particularly important. When I am composing a sermon I always give special care to my first sentence."

"Yes, I suppose that is likely to receive the closest attention from the congregation," said Prendergast, rather unkindly, "but this case is rather different. You can choose your text, but it seems to me that we have to be prepared to answer a question. We're really for the defendant, and we don't know exactly what line the prosecution will take. That's how I see it. What is the first question which the Senators will ask us?"

"There is no doubt about that," said Waterlow. "They will demand with one accord to be shown the University, and they will expect to be led to some vast University building surrounded by a campus. Indeed, if they are youngish Senators they may ask to be shown the campus first. That's rather a teaser for the guide-book, Tennant. Where is the University, and of what does it consist?"

Winn intervened with unusual decision. "They should be told at once that the University is of no real importance at all. It is only a name or an idea or perhaps a convenient generic term which includes all the Colleges. It would really be of no consequence if the University ceased to exist provided that St. Thomas's and Balliol and Christ Church and all the rest continued. These Senators should be told this quite clearly and then shown over St. Thomas's as an example of what an Oxford College is and what it should be. Don't waste any time over the University."

Tennant shook his head. "With respect, Winn," he replied, "I cannot allow that. I know that you are a College man, as indeed I fancy we all are, but we mustn't exaggerate the importance of the Colleges or minimise the value of the University. After all, no one may become a member of a College unless he is also qualified to become a member of the University, and it's the University which gives him his degree at the end of his course. If you were talking to anyone up here, you'd say you were a St. Thomas's man, or that you were at Trinity or Magdalen or wherever it might be; but I think after you'd gone down you'd talk about being at Oxford. It's really all rather difficult, even for a guide-book, but I think Prendergast is right. We ought to start with the University and explain that. Of course, later on when we talk about the lives men live here and the work they do and the games they play, the College comes in more and more and the University less and less. But for a start we have to show that everyone here is a member both of the University and of his College, and I suppose that the Senators will want to know just what this double life means."

"I think that we make too much of the College side," interrupted Pacey. "I remember being told in my youth that *esprit de corps* was the enemy of patriotism. When your loyalty is to a unit or a society which is too small, you are sacrificing much of your utility. Besides, the insistence on College teaching, which seems to me to be a blot on all the non-scientific faculties, surely leads to inefficiency. Think of the ridiculous system of a few years ago when some Colleges actually maintained their own ludicrously ineffective laboratories! I believe that all teaching should be organised by the University, and that the Colleges should be retained only as hostels for the convenient housing of University students. It is the function of the Professors to organise their faculties, and the College tutor is just an anachronism. In a well-organised——"

"Even at the risk of appearing discourteous," exclaimed Winn, "I cannot refrain from observing that this is nonsense, and dangerous nonsense, Pacey. Why, I have been a College tutor for fifty years, and in all that time I hardly remember it being even suggested that the Professors should interfere with the teaching. A Professor should know his place; he ought to lecture and write books, and I suppose supervise the theses of post-graduate students. But, really, to suggest that a Professor should meddle with teaching is Bolshevism—sheer Bolshevism." (2)

A warning gesture from Tennant prevented Pacey from making a retort.

"We are agreed, then, that, though the guide-book will occupy itself almost exclusively with the Colleges, we must dispose of the University first, and I agree that the Senators will demand at once that they should be shown 'the University', and told what it means. Now, how should the guide-book deal with that question? We could, of course, take them to the Registry, but they might think that they had bigger and better Registries in their native land—and we don't want to start them on the wrong lines. Of course, if there were a degree day whilst they were here, it would be easy—we could take them to it, and show them the University at work conferring degrees—but it's vacation and we can't do that. Or we could take them to, say, the Bodleian quadrangle and show them from there the Sheldonian and the Divinity Schools and the Camera and Bodley and All Souls, and all that cluster of buildings which, I suppose, is more 'the University' than any other part of Oxford. Or, again, we could start at the Examination Schools——'

"All of which, I submit," interrupted Gresham, "has been better done by Baedeker and his fellows than by you. No, no, Tennant—to start with the description of University buildings, whether you describe them historically or architecturally or in any other way, is not in the spirit of your undertaking."

"I agree," said Tennant thoughtfully, "but I'm no nearer getting the guide-book under way."

"*Aller Anfang ist schwer*," murmured Waterlow.

"If I may make a suggestion," Gresham went on, "it would be this. We ought, indeed we must, start with a theoretical exposition. Surely the essence of all University teaching is to provide the background of thought and experience on which practical decisions are made. We do not throw the child into the water (though I often think we should) and see if it will swim. We first instruct it in the correct motions for swimming, and then put a hand under its stomach or suspend it from a sort of fishing-rod whilst it makes its early essays at natation. I trust that I make myself quite clear."

"Not in the least," said Trower, "unless you mean that these Senators are not to be allowed in the Bodleian until you have had an opportunity of teaching them to read. And, anyhow, I'm not handling any Senator's stomach."

Gresham sighed. "My dear Trower, you must not underrate your own powers of understanding. Surely my suggestions are perfectly simple and clear. I am proposing that one of our number should deliver a brief address to the Senators on the nature and meaning of the University; he should describe in a few words what it is, how it is governed, and what is its ultimate purpose. I am sure that we should all agree that the person best fitted for this task would be Prendergast, for his legal training will enable him to define precisely, and his great knowledge of the subject will enable him to be short."

"I should have thought that that would have made him deucedly long," growled Trower, who seldom missed an opportunity of stating the obvious.

"On the contrary," replied Gresham, "if I have learned nothing else during my life in Universities, I have at least come to know that only the really learned are capable of conciseness. Anyone can write a long and learned book or lecture—only a master can write a short one with authority and acceptability. You must have a real foundation of knowledge before you can trust yourself to speak shortly on great subjects. The more learned the professor the shorter will be his lecture. For that same reason lectures by young tutors should be given on specialised and detailed subjects; only the older and wiser men should lecture on general or far-reaching topics."

"I incline to agree with you," said Mitton, "for I have often felt that some of the most effective of my sermons have been among the shortest."

"A Philistine," interjected Waterlow, "has been defined as one who is right for the wrong reasons. Which makes me ask the question, Is the *Kulturmensch* the true and exact opposite of the Philistine? That would be a topic on which the Senators might expand."

Tennant was beginning to feel that he was losing his grip of the situation and that he should attempt to regain it.

"I entirely agree with Gresham," he said, "and I support both his plan and his choice of expositor. Indeed, we might carry the suggestion further—as each new topic is raised by the Senators, one or other of us might deliver a little homily or disquisition or even a lecture on it. Now, Prendergast, you must give us a lead. Let us suppose that we are all standing at the end of the Broad or in the shadow of the Camera. The Senators have asked their first question. Where is the University? With a wave or two of the hand I have indicated the Old and the New Bodleian, the Registry, the Sheldonian, and the rest. Winded, but not knocked out, the Senators have countered with their second question, What is the University? With a smile, friendly even if a trifle patronising, you, David Prendergast, step forward and recite your few well-chosen words."

"Well," said Prendergast, "ignoring your unnecessary comments, it would be a quite interesting experiment, and so I don't mind trying my hand—the more so because I can indicate some of the reforms in the University which I am convinced are needed. But I stipulate that nothing I say shall be used in evidence against me."

"Very well—now what is the University?"

Prendergast rose from his seat and took a volume of the *Oxford English Dictionary* from the shelves.

"This, my dear Senators," he began, "is the definition of a University. 'The whole body of teachers and scholars engaged, at a particular place, in giving and receiving instruction in the higher branches of learning; such persons associated together as a society or corporate body, with a definite organization and acknowledged powers and privileges (especially that of conferring degrees), and forming an institution for the promotion of education in the higher or more important branches of learning; also the colleges, buildings, etc., belonging to such a body.' *Chambers*, I think, is more concise. 'A corporation of teachers or assemblage of colleges for teaching the higher branches of learning, and having power to confer degrees.' The Latin word *Universitas* means, unless I am mistaken, a corporation—and so it is a corporation which we are considering. Now you'll notice that the teaching comes first. As I see it, a University comes into being originally by the attraction which great teachers provide. The scholars of the Middle Ages will have journeyed, as they did, to Paris or Padua or Oxford because of the teachers they would find there. That's the primary object of the University. The organisation and the buildings and the degrees (which are, so to speak, the certificates of having studied competently at some particular place) all follow in due course. Here I interrupt my narrative to remark that the older constitutional lawyers used to say that it was part of the prerogative of the Crown to turn any parish in the kingdom into a University. But that hardly affects the question. The dominant note of a University is surely its universality; it is true that the word first referred to the international character of the students gathered at a University, rather than to the universal character of the subjects taught them, but, as Newman argued, the word soon came to mean a place for teaching universal knowledge—it admits all courses and students in all great subjects 'if they come in the name of truth'. If you have an institution for teaching one subject—be it engineering or law or commercial Spanish—you have, in fact, a technical school or institute; for a University the chief gain is the juxtaposition of many subjects and the influence which students of one subject have on those of another. Every student, of course, follows his own course of study, but he gains from living among those who represent all other branches. In a technical school you will get instruction, but in a University you will get education, and that's——"

Gresham interrupted him gently but firmly. "With respect, Prendergast, are you not over-emphasising the teaching and the learning side of University life? I've read my Newman, too, and I well remember his confession of faith: 'If I had to choose between a so-called University, which dispensed with residence and tutorial superintendence, and gave its degrees to any person who passed an examination in a wide range of subjects, and a University which had no Professors, or examinations at all, but merely brought a number of young men together for three or four years, and then sent them away . . . if I was asked which of these two methods was the better discipline of the intellect— mind I do not say which is morally the better, for it is plain that compulsory study must be a good and idleness an intolerable mischief—but if I must determine which of the two courses was the more successful in training, moulding, enlarging the mind, which sent out men the more fitted for their secular duties, which produced better public men, men of the world, men whose names would descend to posterity, I have no hesitation in giving the preference to that University which did nothing, over that which exacted of its members an acquaintance with every science under the sun.' You see what I am driving at? We constantly say that men gain much more here than a mere modicum of learning, and I'm sure that is true. It's all the imponderables that count. If you collect all these young men here together in what Mitton would certainly call the most impressionable years of their lives, they will learn from each other and gain much more than they will get from lectures or tutorials or even from instruction by Pacey in a laboratory. Surely all that's a generally accepted truth. Why go to Oxford at all if you only expect to learn the theory of economics there? You could do that in any place in the world, provided the books were available."

Tennant was by now convinced that his team had got entirely out of hand, and he made a determined effort to reassert his authority.

"The reasons which induce men at any period in history to go to a University, and the gains which come to them from University life—all that's a fascinating subject, but we really mustn't pursue it too far. The Senators, as I see it, having ventured an innocent question about the meaning and the purpose of the University, are by now thoroughly bemused by Prendergast's exposition. I fancy that one or other of them will try to gain time to breathe by asking some other question—hoping, no doubt, to deflect him from the theory of Universities to something more practical. After all, they are not primarily interested in the purpose of University education. They want to know something about Oxford and Oxford life. I suggest that some of us make the imaginative effort necessary to put ourselves in the place of the Senators, and then ask the questions of Prendergast which come into our minds."

"Say, stranger," said Trower, "how is this little old University of yours controlled?"

"You could more easily be forgiven, Trower, for your vulgarity," retorted Tennant, "if it was not so hopelessly Victorian. If you had used the word 'cute', public opinion would have compelled me to dismiss you permanently from the guide-book team. And even as it is I find it hard to forgive you for your woeful imitation of a music-hall American. The word 'controlled' as pronounced by an American (from some States, anyhow) is a curiously beautiful thing. Controlled, controlled—it goes like that. If you had any ear at all you could not murder a beautiful word like an American 'controlled'."

"Is it true, Waterlow," asked Pacey, who had so far remained silent, "that a trained philologist, or indeed a trained student of language, can recognise the exact State on the eastern sea-board from which a citizen of the U.S.A. comes by listening carefully to his speech? You had a couple of years at Washington, didn't you?"

"Well, roughly speaking, I think it could be done by an expert, and all the way from Texas to Maine, but I wouldn't like to be too sure myself. I don't think, for example, that I'd like to back myself to be awfully sure as between, say, Georgia and the Carolinas."

"As the governor of North Carolina said to the governor of South Carolina," murmured Mitton with a reproachful glance at Gresham.

"I apprehend and apologise," said Gresham with a smile, as he pushed the decanter towards the Chaplain.

It was now Prendergast's turn to lodge a protest.

"I began," he said, "what I am entitled, I think, to describe as a well-thought-out and ably constructed lecture. I was interrupted by some of my hearers in a manner which I can only describe as frivolous. I entirely refuse to bandy words with the Senators about the relative merits of the accent of Virginia or Boston. Either, my dear Robert, I continue and complete my lecture without interruptions, or—or I sulk."

"A very reasonable ultimatum, and of course we choose the former alternative."

"Very well then," continued Prendergast. "I will return to the point where I broke off, but let me make it quite clear that if I require any Senatorial stimulus, I shall provide it myself and not rely on Trower. For I begin to get these Senators into my mind. I know not if, 'aiming a fancy, I rightly divine' that the three Senators are men of widely different natures and upbringing. It appears to me that one is a scholarly Senator, with an honours degree to his credit somewhere in his past history, and one is a political Senator, interested in organisation and such-like, and the third a muscular Senator, one who years ago pitched for some famous baseball team or rowed in a well-known crew. Very well then—that is the audience to which I must address myself, and those are the men who will throw in their questions if I do not make myself readily understandable."

He paused for a moment to regain the thread of his argument.

"Now, gentlemen, I shall say, you understand the purpose of the University—and here I shall make one of those encouraging circular motions with my right hand, such as are used by all lecturers to indicate that they are not very sure of their facts and propose to pass rapidly to another topic. You understand the purpose of the University—but that, indeed, is the purpose of all Universities. What you want to know is how Oxford is peculiar —in what way it differs from other Universities—or, in other words, wherein its special excellence lies. And so at once I must explain to you that Oxford is both a residential University and one in which the undergraduates are members not only of the University but also of the various Colleges which themselves make up the University."

"Precisely," said Winn, "as I remarked at the commencement, the College system——"

Tennant interrupted him. "I'm sorry, Winn, but I promised

Prendergast that he should conclude his lecture without interruption. I'm sure he'll do justice to the merits of the College system in general and St. Thomas's in particular."

"No sane man ever let a lawyer speak without interruption," objected Trower, who was not in the best of tempers; but his remark passed unheeded, and Prendergast continued.

"I find it a little difficult to choose the best method of describing the double life, or rather the double loyalty, of the Oxford undergraduate. I was tempted at one time to draw a parallel with a citizen of the U.S.A. who was also, of course, a citizen of Ohio or Massachusetts or some other State; but I reflected that my political Senator would know far too much about the comparative importance of State and Union rights and duties, and, after all, it is the first law of the lecturer to avoid speaking about subjects on which the audience is better informed than himself. I shall, therefore, take a different illustration. Gentlemen, I shall say, Oxford affords an exact parallel to the old Holy Roman Empire—about the construction of which it would be impertinent of me to remind you. Just as Bavaria and Saxony and Brandenburg and the rest were within the Empire, and paid contributions both in money and men for Imperial purposes, so do the Colleges contribute to the University. It goes without saying, however, that when we turn to the individual men, who are members both of the University and of their own College, their allegiance and loyalty to the latter are by far the closer and more important."

"Precisely," said Winn, "as I——" But Prendergast disregarded him.

"Was there not an old Swiss proverb—or was it Bavarian—'my shirt is nearer to me than my coat'? Very well then, to be a member of Oriel or Hertford or St. Thomas's means a great deal; that the undergraduate is also a member of the University is often forgotten. None the less, the University does impinge on the lives of the undergraduates, as I see it, in three ways. It provides examinations, it confers degrees, and it exercises a somewhat loose and precarious discipline. With these three aspects I, or some other of us, shall deal in good time. But also the University has become a great self-governing corporation, a great owner of property, and perhaps a great social and political power.

"That is the moment, I fancy, when the political Senator will interrupt with a better-worded variant of Trower's question. 'How, Sir,' he will enquire, 'is this University governed and controlled, and how far does it conform to true democratic principles?'" He paused to help himself to a glass of wine.

"Good," said Tennant. "That is the right line. I, too, am seeing these three Senators more and more clearly; indeed, I am beginning to call them by their Christian names. The scholarly Senator is named Porson, the athletic Senator I address as Samson, and I fancy that his intimates call the political Senator Aristotle, with the accent strongly on the 'tot', but——"

"At the risk of appearing pedantic," Winn interrupted, "and at the greater risk of being prevented by my juniors from finishing the sentence which I have been permitted to begin, I feel that I owe it to the reputation which (I flatter myself) we enjoy in this Common Room for accuracy of language to protest against the misuse, or at the best looseness of phraseology, which is implicit in the use of the term 'Christian name'. Surely no scholar would venture to call Aristotle a Christian name—and I have my doubts about Porson."

"I entirely agree. I should have said 'first name'. But, as I was saying, I believe that I know these Senators even better than Prendergast. Aristotle, I fancy, is a bachelor whose life has been devoted to the intricacies of American politics and perhaps of American law. Prendergast will be able to satisfy his desire for information, though it might be prudent to present him with a copy of the University Statutes, so that he may clear up for himself any little point which seems obscure. But Porson and Samson are both, I am sure, fathers of families, and probably both are contemplating sending a son or sons to Oxford. Their questions will be determined by their wish to know what Oxford and Oxford life are like. But, Prendergast, you have the word, and we promised you no interruptions."

"As I recollect," said Prendergast, "but I am a long-suffering man—and, in addition, I want to continue my really admirable lecture before I forget what I intended to say. Now, let me see, I was faced by the question 'How is the University controlled, and is it a truly democratic institution?'.

"I think that my brother lawyers would support me if I said that the University is a self-governing corporation, and that effective authority is supposed to be in the hands of the Congregation of the University. At this point I shall deftly but decisively decline an invitation from Senator Aristotle to compare our constitution with that of an American University. The University is, no doubt, a non-sovereign or subordinate law-making body, and it adapts itself to changing conditions by changes of statute and decrees of Congregation. That it is keenly jealous of its independence of outside authorities I hardly need to remind you. Congregation, then, would seem to be the key institution, and Congregation consists of such members of Convocation as are teachers, administrators, or officials in the University. At this juncture I shall certainly have to employ my most sweeping gesture in order to prevent Aristotle from questioning me on the exact functions of Congregation and Convocation. That information, I shall say, you can readily obtain from the Statutes. In brief, Congregation, about 1,000 strong, is the body we have to consider, and it is primarily a legislative body. And yet Congregation really plays but a small part in University life. The really effective body is Council. Now, Council is a legislative as well as an executive body; for example, every measure presented to Congregation is initiated by Council. You may think of it, if you will, as a sort of Cabinet, with the Vice-Chancellor presiding over it as a kind of Prime Minister. I think that must suffice as a very rough picture for the Senators, for I mustn't venture into the labyrinths of boards and committees and such-like. Will that do, Tennant, and can I get down?"

"Not yet, you haven't answered the second question. Have we a democratic form of government?"

"Ah yes. That is not so easy as it appears at first. Council is freely elected, and so it ought to be a representative body responsible to Congregation, but I'm bound to confess that it always appears to me rather a bogus sort of democracy. How many of us take the faintest interest in the meetings of Congregation or even in the work of Council? It's true that we can vote when there are vacancies, and even that we do vote if a St. Thomas's man happens to be a candidate, but for the most part our attitude is that those who are interested in University politics are welcome to run them, provided only that they don't impinge on College autonomy. That may be sound enough, but it isn't democracy—or is it? Perhaps the same sort of thing happens in most communities; power falls actually and inevitably into the hands of those who desire to wield it."

"But," said Mitton, "I think that you are evading the question. You will not tell us if Council and its control of the University is really a good thing. Now, that is a moral question, and I think that the guide-book ought to face it squarely."

"But I can't face it," replied Prendergast, "because I don't know the answer. As a life-long Liberal I demand that all opinions should be represented on Council in proportion to their strength —I require that all controversial issues should come to full and free debate in Congregation—I maintain that all our institutions should be logically and argumentatively defensible. On the other hand, as a practical Conservative, especially in University affairs,

I think precisely the opposite, for as such it seems to me that imperfect institutions which work are immeasurably better than theoretically better ones which don't. In other words, I like to think that our life moves along very happily if Council is allowed to proceed on the familiar lines without undue interference, and I must admit that the suggestion that I should embroil myself in the mysterious proceedings of Congregation is abhorrent to me. But I'm not the person to whom the Senators should have addressed this question. Gresham, you were on Council for a year or two, as I well remember; you ought to know whether it's what Mitton calls a good thing or not. Can't you draw a vivid picture of Council which brings it before the mental vision of the Senators?"

Gresham smiled and polished his glasses thoughtfully.

"I would much rather do that," he said, "than attempt to give a clear answer to the original question. It seems to me, and I've made this point before, that we tend to shy at every opportunity from our real purpose, which is to provide guide-book information for the Senators. Surely we ought to say in the grand manner something like this. The whole control of the multifarious activities of the University is in the hands of Council. This body, which is elected according to the strictest democratic principles, is composed of self-sacrificing and assiduous men who devote their working hours to the business of the University. That's enough, surely, on the constitutional issue. But to make it vivid we want more than words. In our education of these eminent visitors, don't let us forget the visual aids. I should keep them on the move—let them see the Divinity School and the Sheldonian and the Congregation House whilst we are telling of degrees and meetings and so forth, and show them the Delegates' room to make the nature of Council clear to them."

"That's sound enough," said Tennant. "Samson, at any rate, will be a heavy man, and a little physical exhaustion in the early stages can do nothing but good, for it will certainly stifle in-convenient questions. None the less, I think you might come clean about Council, if only to satisfy our curiosity."

"Well, I don't think that I was ever really fitted for Council, but that is neither here nor there. I do think that Mitton's question should receive an affirmative answer. It's an efficient body—too efficient for me, perhaps."

"What exactly do you mean by that?"

Gresham's favourite phrase was used at once. "Let me be more explicit," he replied. "I shall show to the Senators the Delegates' room, and they will admire it, for it is in a manner beautiful and impressive. Dominating it, too, is a portrait of Queen Anne, which seemed to set the form of Council's proceedings. You see, I always felt that she was there as a sort of standing reminder to us of her own demise and as a perpetual encouragement to us to busy ourselves with such matters as have become urgent since that unhappy event. But I mustn't weary you with my fancies. The room is big and narrow—so long and so narrow that it is quite impossible for most of those present to hear very much of what goes on—and that, of course, makes for efficiency."

"Why 'of course'?" demanded Trower; "I should have thought that would have led to hopeless inefficiency."

"Far from it. No body could have been more efficient or more expeditious than Council in my day. Any business was shortly explained by the Vice-Chancellor or his deputy, but since I could never hear what was said, I soon observed that everything was passed by general agreement long before I or the majority of those present had appreciated the point at issue. There was hardly any opposition and never any unnecessary criticism. One must think well of a body where no one thinks of speaking unless he has something of value to contribute. There were other para-doxes, too, which all, to my mind, made for efficiency."

Trower intervened rather ponderously.

"At the risk of being considered obtuse, may I beg you once more to be explicit?"

"Gladly. I was told, for example, when my vote was solicited for some lawyer that the presence of a lawyer on Council was, in view of the many legal points which arose, a prime necessity. Once I had joined Council I was speedily converted to the more orthodox view that the presence of two lawyers was absolutely essential."

"Good," said Prendergast, a little too quickly, "but what brought you to that very sound conclusion?"

"Because," said Gresham sweetly, "the two lawyers were always in fundamental disagreement, and so they cancelled each other out. Business, you know, is never so smoothly and efficiently done as when the legal aspects are entirely ignored. Any deliberative assembly gets on famously if there are no lawyers present, and it gets on well enough if there are two, but one lawyer without a rival spells disaster. (3) There were other paradoxes, too. Take science, for example. Every scientist in Oxford has told me at one time or another that science is hopelessly under-represented on Council and that that is a major scandal. But what did I find? Simply this. That three-quarters or more of the time of our deliberations was devoted to scientific matters, and that the scientists seldom if ever failed to get their way. I assure you that though the pension of a University bedel or some such matter might lead to debate and even to disagreement, millions of money and acres of land could be apportioned to scientific purposes without a hint of dissent. And why? Just because the scientists were not represented. Doctors of Divinity and Professors of Literature will always support any scientific motion if a sufficiently formidable demand is put before them, partly because they can't ask intelligent questions about the details and partly because they pride themselves on their broad-mindedness. A dark hint that the women's vote for the measure in Congregation is secure is sufficient to stifle any lingering doubts. Believe me, there are wise men amongst the scientists of Oxford; they know well enough that if you want your way in a representative or democratic body you must take care not to be represented. You will find your champions easily enough, and they will never be suspect, as your representatives would be. A cynic (which I am not) would declare that in a democratic society wire-pulling will beat representation any time. But I was speaking of Council as an institution——"

"You *were*," said Tennant with decision. "But I think that we must stick to the past tense. I'm not wholly sure that it would be beneficial for the Senators, or that it would redound to the reputation of the University, to say more about the activities of Council. I think we ought to pass on."

Winn had been silent for some time, but he now made an urgent request. "Whilst we are showing these gentlemen the University buildings," he said, "I do think it incumbent on us to show them that historic spot where Charles II's Parliament was held—particularly because the incident arouses much fascinating speculation."

"Did Charles II hold a Parliament in Oxford?" enquired Pacey.

Winn tried to conceal his surprise and disapproval, but without very much success.

"My dear Pacey, you must know at least in the barest outline the history of that episode, for it was of the greatest importance in the history of the seventeenth century. Indeed, I sometimes think that there is no moment in our history when the influence and importance of Oxford in the national life was more vividly displayed or more clearly shown. There is also no episode which serves as a better example of the difficulties which face the honest and laborious historian. Now, let me see, where was I? Oh yes. Parliament in Oxford. There was a so-called Parliament here of

course in 1258, and in 1625, if I have the date correctly, Charles I
held a Parliament in Oxford. Was it not because the plague was
raging in London? Yes, I'm sure that is so. Yes, let me see, the
Commons sat in the Divinity School, and the Lords in the
Picture Gallery of the Bodleian, and the Privy Council met at
Christ Church. I think I have the details correct. But the Parliament of 1681, that——"

Tennant never displayed towards Winn the same critical or
commanding tone which he used towards the rest of his colleagues, but he found it necessary to venture a mild protest.

"I know that these seventeenth-century scenes are full of
fascination for you and indeed for us, but I wonder whether we
can expect the Senators to appreciate them. Don't you think we
should pass on to some new topic?"

Waterlow, however, came to Winn's support.

"With respect, Mr. Editor, I'm entirely of Winn's opinion
in this matter, for I recall a story my father used to tell of President
Roosevelt. Theodore, or Teddy, of course, and not Franklin D. .
My father was showing the President over Christ Church, and
I'm doing no injustice to either when I say that both of them
were profoundly bored. This, my father would say, is by
Reynolds, and a very fine example of his work, and this by
Romney and much admired. And the President was saying 'Oh',
or its American equivalent, at intervals without much conviction.
That at least is how I picture the scene, and it appears to me that
the Senators may well repeat their former President's performance
at a later date. But, to quote you, my dear Winn, where was I? Oh
yes, I was in the Christ Church Senior Common Room, and my
father, a little exhausted but still putting up a game fight, pointed
to a double row of engravings and photographs. 'There,' said he,
'are portraits of members of the House who became Governors-
General or Viceroys of India—Wellesley, and Dalhousie, and
Canning, and all the rest of them.' 'What!' said Roosevelt.

'What!! Do you tell me that all those Viceroys came from this one College?' 'Indeed I do', said my father. And then the whole scene changed, and he could hardly keep pace with all the President's questions and enquiries. I suppose that, in fact, Roosevelt saw in a flash that Oxford wasn't just the museum of antiquities which he had supposed it to be, but a nursery of great men. I don't need to labour the point, do I? When I go into the Bodleian quadrangle, I marvel at the beauty of the Divinity School, or I wonder whether Wren had much influence in the building of the Old Ashmolean, or, even more probably, I try to imagine how Bodley himself could ever have persuaded the more conservative of the University authorities of his day to allow him to absorb all the Schools into his great library—but I do not believe that the Senators would be more than distantly though politely interested in any of those things. But make them see how Oxford history is intertwined with the history of England; let them feel that English kings have stood where they are standing; make them see a picture of Charles II facing his Parliament, and I'll lay you a reasonable wager that they'll remember more of Winn's account of that incident than they will even of Prendergast's admirable discussion on the constitution of the University. Now, Winn, you had just remarked that Charles II had summoned a Parliament in Oxford in 1681. There's your cue from the prompter and your long speech follows, as the B.B.C. would say, almost immediately."

A little dazed, Winn continued his narration.

"I suppose that I ought to have mentioned that Charles II had had a Parliament in Oxford previously—namely in 1665—again because of the plague, but I will not pause over that, for it is the Parliament of 1681 with which I am primarily concerned.

"Few of you will need to be reminded that the short but eventful session of the 1681 Parliament was opened on Monday, March 21. [Pacey smiled sardonically.] The Lords sat in the

Geometry School and the Commons in the Convocation House. Three days were spent in the swearing-in of members, and business did not actually commence till the Thursday, when the Opposition attempted to revive the waning credit of the Popish Plot. The Commons also complained of the inadequacy of the accommodation provided for them, and Charles himself spent some time on the Saturday in discussing the arrangements for transferring them to the newly completed Sheldonian Theatre. All that is clear enough, the doubt arises with regard to the dramatic dissolution on Monday, March 28. On that day the King was carried in a sedan-chair to the Lords; in a second chair were carried his robes of state. The Commons were summoned to the bar of the House of Lords, and the King called upon the Chancellor to declare his will. Lord Nottingham announced that the Parliament was dissolved. It has always been supposed that this famous scene was enacted in the Geometry School, and the place is pointed out to this day. That would be the inference both from the account given by Anthony Wood and, I think, from the Journals of the two Houses. Yet Thomas Bruce, afterwards 2nd Earl of Ailesbury, states categorically in his Memoirs that the session on that Monday was held in Christ Church. 'About 11,' he writes, 'I went to Christ Church, the Parliament sitting in great rooms within the precincts of the College.'

"So you will realise," Winn went on, "that I am tortured by doubt. Can it be that the most famous occurrence connected with Bodley never happened there at all? In vain I balance probabilities. Is it not true that the Geometry School would have been too small to hold even some few of the members of the Commons as well as the Lords, and that I should therefore consider the Christ Church site as the more probable? Is it not also true that tradition in such matters is seldom at fault, and that—apart from Bruce—no mention is made by anyone of a change from the arrangements of the previous week? I still hope that further research may settle this controversy, which I consider to be of the first importance, but for the time being I own that I am sadly perplexed."

Winn paused, a little flushed by his exertions. "Really," he said, "I cannot regret the discussions we have had about the guide-book, if it has led to some of you taking an interest in historical problems of this kind. I wish that one or other of you would feel disposed to pursue the matter further, and perhaps settle some of the controversial points."

"We've only six days for the guide-book, and we really must move on. Haven't we spent long enough in the Bodleian quadrangle and among the University buildings? I admit when I think of Winn and the Parliament of 1681 I feel a little like the Red Queen seizing Alice by the hand, and crying, 'Faster, faster' all the time. But you'll forgive me, Winn, I know, for we must hurry if we're ever going to get to the eighth square, where it's all feasting and fun."

Unexpectedly it was Pacey who raised a protest at this suggestion.

"I've listened patiently," he said, "to the account of a Parliament which took place, as I understand, before and not after the death of Queen Anne, but I've not forgotten that Prendergast was telling us about the government and business of the University. Now, that subject does seem to me to be really important, and I agree that the present system is totally unsatisfactory. You told us, Prendergast, that you had ideas of your own about University Reform. What are they?"

Prendergast laughed. "I was afraid that those rash words of mine might be a sort of boomerang. Frankly, as the discussion has gone on I have come more and more to the conclusion that all is very well as it is and that reform can well be postponed. But I won't avoid the issue. If you'll let me, I'll conclude my lecture—if any of you still remember that I was delivering a lecture—by an indication of the lines on which, as I think, reform should proceed, though I cannot pretend to make my proposals with any great conviction.

"As I see it the main fault of the present system is that only a very few take any interest at all in the affairs of the University. We can treat that cynically, and say that things will go very well so long as no one worries about them. 'Leave well alone, and ever leave ill alone. Are you the tradesmen to tinker leaky vessels in England?' as Carlyle once remarked. There's truth and wisdom in that. Still, it can't be quite healthy to let things slide as we do. It's a platitude—or a truth, for the words are often synonymous—that it's better for people to be interested in their own government, than for them to accept without question even the most perfect form of government. The prime necessity, then, is for more of us to take an active interest."

"I beg to register my whole-hearted dissent," said Gresham. "I believe that the true purpose of the University is study and the interchange of ideas, and that anything that distracts the mind from learning is detrimental to us. Let us be thankful that there are persons in Oxford who will shoulder the business of administration and leave us free to pursue our proper course. To be quite explicit, I should say that the College tutor was never intended to be a Martha; the way of Mary is the way for him."

"That is a point of view which I respect," said Prendergast, "but I'm briefed just now for the other side. Isn't it true that all the great changes of the last twenty or thirty years have been carried out without most of us being conscious of them until they had taken place? Think of the building of the New Bodleian— and, by the way, we must show the Senators that as well as the Old Bodleian. I seem to remember that I thought at the time that the only sane thing to do was to construct an immense underground dump a mile or two from the centre of the City and have all the unwanted or seldom-wanted books there with motor transport to bring them in if required. Yet my clear recollection is that the only opportunity I had of expressing my opinion was by recording a vote for either scheme A or scheme B—with both of which I was profoundly dissatisfied. Or think of the purchase of properties by the University. No doubt the policy of acquiring real property is a sound one, but can any of you say that you have ever heard the question fully debated or had any opportunity of expressing an opinion about what is, surely, an important question of policy? Or again I think of the Parks. Every two or three years another slice of open land disappears, and a new and vast modern laboratory springs up where once was green grass and trees."

"You cannot criticise that," expostulated Pacey. "No modern University worthy of the name can fail to make some provision for the growing needs of science."

"Don't misunderstand me," Prendergast replied. "I admit without question that the science departments should and must expand. What I maintain is that we ought to carry out great changes of that sort with our eyes open. I can well remember walking in the Parks with you, Winn, some years ago, when you expressed surprise that there were new laboratories where you had not observed them before, and where you said that you had always understood (though how or why I don't know) that the claims of science on the Parks had been satisfied and that there would be no more encroachments. Now, I do not for a moment regret the advance of science, but I do think that the whole University should have been conscious of the need for these changes and have discussed and approved them as they occurred. In present conditions such things just happen, and only the truly virtuous and conscientious inform themselves of what is occurring or about to occur. Believe me, we ought to take a closer and a better-informed interest in the affairs of our own University."

Pacey nodded in rather half-hearted agreement, but as a persistent man he was clearly not satisfied.

73

"Admitted," he said, "that members of Congregation ought to take this interest, how do you propose to ensure that they should? You can't coerce people into doing the right thing. What practical proposal would you make to meet the difficulty?"

"That's a fair point," replied Prendergast. "I cannot, at the end of my lecture, produce a scheme for the reform of University government and business, but I will indicate the sort of minor changes with which I should begin. First I should change the time at which Congregation meets. Two o'clock on a Tuesday afternoon is an impossible time. Why shouldn't we meet at half-past eight in the evening instead? With the eye of faith, I seem to see a tradition growing up according to which all Fellows would dine on Tuesdays and proceed together to Congregation afterwards. And then I'd have the *Oxford Magazine*, or some such periodical, give a balanced account of the measures to be debated and the issues to be raised at the next meeting of Congregation. An individual's interest in public affairs is a tender plant which needs encouragement. Only a minority will master the details of the *Gazette*. And then I'd simplify procedure as much as possible and make it easy for anyone to intervene. That means that I should study the interests of the back-benchers. But before I did any of those things I should make a small change, which would, I believe, be more effective in making University business a reality than any of the other innovations which I have mentioned. I should abolish the use of Latin in all of our proceedings."

Winn shuddered. "I cannot believe that you mean that seriously," he said. "All our old traditions are based on the use of Latin. I still feel a thrill when the Vice-Chancellor calls for the vote. '*Placetne vobis Domini Doctores, placetne vobis Magistri.*' When I was young we had a non-placet society, pledged to vote '*non*' on every issue. Now that was both theoretically and practically sound. Our society was based on the belief that any proposal brought forward by Council was bound to involve change, that

74

change was to be resisted by right-thinking people, and that we could therefore safely vote '*nonplacet*' without wasting time on a study of the arguments advanced. No, no, Prendergast, you as a lawyer should know better than to put your impious hands on the long-standing usages of the University."

Prendergast laughed. "I assure you," he said, "that I am wholly serious in making this proposal. If you want men to participate in public business you must make it easy for them to do so. The very fact that a small but important part of the Statutes are in Latin makes it laborious and tiresome to ascertain how the University is controlled. You know well enough that at all our own College meetings we make constant reference to our Statutes; all of us know them tolerably well, and everyone is concerned to see that we keep within them. But you could count on the fingers of one hand those who are really familiar with the Statutes of the University. Besides, I have always felt that it is something of an insult to our mother tongue to use Latin for ceremonial purposes. Is it even dignified ? The last time I went to a University ceremony was for the installation of a Vice-Chancellor or the admission of proctors or some such occasion, and as I walked back to St. Thomas's the only comment made to me by my companion was that he believed that the Vice-Chancellor had been guilty of two false quantities. But English—think of what could be done with that!"

Unexpectedly Gresham at this point declared himself on the side of reform.

"I yield to no one," he said, "in my reverence and respect for Latin. The study of it is, I believe, the foundation of every sound system of education. For teaching precision of thought and economy in the use of words it has no equal; nor do I believe that the profitable study of modern languages or history or law, or English literature for that matter, is possible without it. Latin is the basis of our Western European civilisation. Yet for all that I agree with Prendergast. It seems to me that English can rise to the same level of dignity and beauty as Latin of the golden age. For my part, I should rejoice to hear the Public Orator declaiming in English—the more so if he would first have some private tuition from a Professor of Elocution. I remember, if you will allow me to digress for a moment, a meeting of a College club which I attended as an undergraduate, because it helps to illustrate what I am trying to say. It was a literary club, and we took ourselves very seriously—nor would it be unfair to add that the standard of our papers and discussions was a high one. In one term our Provost, himself a former member of the Club, persuaded Robert Bridges to read a paper to us. The usual polite letters were exchanged, and I remember that we were a little dashed when the great man informed us that he would read a paper on Prosody."

"May a simple soldier ask exactly what prosody is?" asked Trower.

"He may, for at that time some of the less intellectual of our number asked the same question. One definition is that it is 'that part of grammar which treats of quantity, accent, and the laws of verse or versification'; another, that it is 'the science of the quantity of syllables and of pronunciation as affecting versification'. The O.E.D says simply 'the science of versification; that part of the study of language which deals with the forms of metrical composition'. So now, my dear Bursar, you are informed.

"We spent some time in studying the subject, and I think most of us composed speeches on different aspects of the subject so that the discussion should at least not bring the club into discredit. The appointed night arrived, and I well recall the appearance of the poet and the Provost when they entered the room. Robert Bridges, you know, was to many of us the most impressive man in Oxford at that time. You might see him striding across Magdalen Bridge on a sunny morning, tall and athletic in spite of his age, with a full beard which the most romantic of Victorian poets might have envied, and on his head a grey sombrero with a brim so wide that no lesser man could have carried it—a majestic man, at once masculine, sensitive, and poetic. There was to me something Elizabethan or Shakespearian about his outward mien. Yet our Provost, the older man of the two, was little if at all inferior to him—or so at least we thought. He, too, wore a full beard, once a flaming gold, but by then almost entirely white. You saw him at his best when, in the scarlet robes of a Doctor of Divinity, he would proceed through Gloucester Green to carry out his duties as Clerk of the Market. How right it was, in Oxford if nowhere else, that a Doctor of Divinity, appropriately clad, should inspect the weighing of butter and beef! A fine man, and a gentle man in the true sense; you can see a portrait of him by Charles Furse in Hall to-day. It's unfinished but it does him justice, and to my judgment it's as good a picture as Furse ever painted."

"I remember him well," said Winn. "I used to regret that he was not a St. Thomas's man."

"What higher praise could be given? Well, into our club meeting these two great veterans came, and after the usual courtesies Bridges began to read his paper. Unfortunately for us, it was not, in the ordinary sense of the word, a paper at all. He had been engaged for some time in writing verse in hexameters, and what he did that night was to read aloud to us a great many of his own lines without any unnecessary pause or comment. When he finished we were a little abashed, for our prepared comments on prosody seemed out of place; the discussion was in plain terms almost a fiasco."

Gresham paused and it seemed to Tennant that the story had ended.

"I enjoyed the tale," he said, "but I don't quite understand how it affects the question of the use of Latin."

Gresham smiled. "How stupid of me," he said, "I have omitted the whole point of the anecdote. When I said that Bridges only read his own lines and added no commentary, I was not being strictly accurate. Two or three times he raised his beard from the book out of which he was reading, and repeated a line which he had just read or interpolated a sentence of criticism. One of those rare aberrations from his text I shall always remember. 'My brother,' he said, 'my brother—wonderful words, Virgil could never have done anything to equal that!' The end of the evening I remember too. 'Well, Provost,' said the poet, when our poor little starveling discussion had petered out, 'how did you like my paper?' Even College loyalty and veneration for the Head of our Society had not been able to blind us to the fact that the Provost had composed himself to rest at the beginning of the evening and had slumbered quietly and peacefully until the end. He was, however, equal to the occasion. 'I'm sorry to say,' he replied, 'that I seem to grow deafer and deafer. I really couldn't hear a great deal of it in this large room.' 'Never mind,' said Bridges, 'we'll walk over to your Lodgings and I'll read it to you again.'"

"I suppose he was getting his own back on the Provost," suggested Trower. Gresham hesitated. "No," he said at length, "I really don't think so. It seemed to me that as a creative artist he felt that he had read something which was really good, and he didn't wish his old friend to lose it. The writers and the lecturers of that day had a healthy belief in the merit of their own work— that was one of their great advantages. I used to go myself to the lectures of one of the best-known of ancient historians, and I went in company with an undergraduate friend who belonged to the lecturer's own College. He's a bishop now, so the story must be true. Years afterwards he told me that, missing one of the lectures, he called on the lecturer, who was also his tutor, to apologise. 'I am very sorry,' he said, 'that through mischance

78

I missed your lecture this morning.' 'You missed a great deal,' was the reply. 'I am, if I may say so, always good, but this morning I surpassed myself. Good-day to you.'"

Winn nodded agreement. "It was a generation of good lecturers because they believed in the value of what they were saying. I remember that Arthur Johnson, who was one of the great pillars of the Modern History school in my early days and who taught in half a dozen Colleges, used to bring our hearts into our mouths by the reckless manner in which he crossed the High on his way to and from his lecture; we always thought he would be run over. When someone expostulated with him he replied that he was oblivious of the traffic. 'I never go to deliver a lecture,' he said, 'without thinking what a wonderful occasion it will be, and I never come back without thinking how much better I might have made it.' I fear he could not cross the High now with impunity were he still alive."

"The state of the traffic in the High is a serious matter," said Pacey, "but it ought not to be beyond us to resolve it if we adopt a scientific approach to the problem."

"Order, order," replied Tennant. "Traffic problems are *not* in the agenda; the use of Latin in University business is. Does the guide-book give the great weight of its authority to Prendergast's veto on Latin, or does it not? 'Is it your pleasure, learned Doctors, is it your pleasure, regent masters?' Come, Winn, doesn't that form satisfy you as well as your '*placets*' and your '*nons*'? Those in favour say Aye."

A chorus of 'ayes' did not quite drown Winn's '*nonplacet*'. "You will at least," he implored, "maintain Latin for the conferring of honorary degrees?"

"Most certainly not," said Prendergast. "I appear, temporarily at least, to have a majority, and that advantage I shall ruthlessly exploit. I feel myself that the Latin speeches made when the Honorands are presented should entirely disappear. I know

79

how carefully they are composed, I know that their Latinity is beyond criticism, I know that the Public Orator uses ingenuity and skill of a high order. But I cannot get out of my mind that Latin addresses of that kind are a sort of game; they are on a par with, say, the epilogue at a Westminster play. It's a learned game, but still a game. And then the convention that a learned jest or humorous reference must occur in a majority of these speeches. Would these remarks appear worthy of the dignity of the occasion if they were expressed in English? And do they become worthy just because they are disguised in a dead language? The Honorands don't understand the speeches, unless translations are provided, as sometimes they are, and the majority of the audience does not either. No, no; let us have the music and dignity of the English of the Prayer Book. I'll warrant that some of the compliments which are paid by a Public Orator of the future in his mother tongue are remembered when the Latin quips of his predecessors have long been sunk in oblivion."

"I thought someone would soon bring up the Prayer Book," said Waterlow, "but I expected that Mitton would be the culprit. Surely we are going on too far and too fast. Let us start any hare, but don't let us hunt the creature to death. Why should we not explain the ceremony to the Senators, and await their comments?"

"Exactly," agreed Tennant. "We will take Porson and Samson and Aristotle into the Sheldonian and make the Encænia live for them. We'll describe the procession and the music and the thronged seats, and show them where the Chancellor sits if he is present, and all the traditional ceremonial of the proctors and the rest. Then, with a little subtle flattery, we'll suggest that they may one day be themselves recipients of honorary degrees, and we'll ask if they would prefer to find themselves addressed in Latin or in English. We'll make them the jury, in fact. Isn't that a fair compromise?"

Winn, though easily swayed by argument, had a fund of obstinacy where his special interests were concerned.

"I have little acquaintance," he said rather stiffly, "with the New World, but I shall, indeed, have a poor opinion of American culture if these gentlemen show themselves in any way sympathetic to your really quite outrageous proposals."

"To my mind," said Waterlow, "we have arrived at the moment where we should adjourn, or as Trower would certainly say, call it a day. *Morgen ist auch ein Tag*, you know, though, I fear, if Robert had his way, that *Morgen* will not see the end of our labours nor *Uebermorgen* either."

CHAPTER III

"ONE of the remarks which impressed me last night," said Tennant, "was Gresham's when he was speaking of Council. He said that we must not neglect the visual aids in our education of the Senators. That's true, I'm sure. Our theories and our descriptions of manners and customs will be much more effective if we can attach them to scenes or objects which the Senators can themselves observe. All of us, at one time or another, must have shown visitors round Oxford, and I suppose that most of us from our undergraduate days onwards have made some particular sight or view a speciality of our own."

Gresham shook his head in dissent. "Personally I never showed a visitor round Oxford in my life. My habit was always to invite a Rhodes Scholar to undertake that task for me; he always did it so much better than I could have done."

"Still," continued Tennant, "you must have some favourite scene or some view of Oxford in which you take special pleasure. At any rate, I shall assume that you have. Here, then, is my proposal for to-night. Let each of us in turn lead the Senators to some chosen view-point; let him show it to them; and let him then use it to describe and discuss some particular aspect of Oxford life. Perhaps I don't really mean a view—it's rather a matter of *Sehenswürdigkeiten*, of things which they ought to see because they are peculiar to Oxford and because they are incentives to thought or discussion."

"I'm inclined to think that a good plan," said Trower. "It seems to me that this isn't going to be a guide-book at all if we don't have some description. To my mind, we did nothing last night except collect material for some dullish lectures on University business."

"I'm afraid, Robert, that I'm rather dubious about your proposed programme," objected Waterlow. "A beautiful view seems to me to be something which should be looked at and admired rather than discussed. The better the view the less I feel inclined to describe it. Do you know the old but, I think, apposite story of the two Scotsmen who were shown the falls of Niagara by an enthusiastic American. 'And what comes to your mind,' he asked, 'when you contemplate this amazing, this unique spectacle of the power and might of nature ?' 'Aweel,' came the answer, 'I minds me of a peahen at Ballachulish with three legs.' The American raised his hands to heaven, and turned to the second Scot—'You, Sir,' he said, 'if I judge correctly, are not a soulless bonehead whose mind is concerned with three-legged peahens. What great thoughts come into your mind when you watch this mighty mass of water precipitating itself into the vast abyss below ?' 'Aye, and what's to prevent it ?' was the answer he received. You know, I have an uneasy suspicion that if I expend the treasures of my eloquence on the beauties of Magdalen Tower on May morning the only reaction I shall get from Samson or Porson will be a question why Magdalen Oxford has one 'e' less than her sister of Cambridge."

"At one time our Magdalen was almost invariably spelt with the final 'e'," observed Winn, who was always interested in historical minutiæ. "Certainly, for example, by Ingram in his *Memorials*, and I fancy later still. I wish that I knew when the usage changed—I must try to find out."

It was Prendergast who salvaged Tennant's programme for the evening. "I feel sure that John has overlooked one great advantage of your plan," he said. "We are eight, and that means that each of us can enjoy idleness and leisure while the other seven are talking. Personally I'll gladly make my own inadequate contribution if I am excused duty for the other seven periods."

There was general agreement in this view, and Tennant turned to Winn with the request that he, as the senior, should address the company first.

"There can be no doubt," began Winn, "that the most striking as well as the most beautiful and historic of all Oxford views is a view of St. Thomas's. There is nothing to compare with it. I am, however, very much exercised in my mind to decide exactly which view of the College or from the College I should ask the Senators to observe first. The view of the Hall with the Library and Chapel partly visible beyond is magnificent, but there is something to be said for taking them first to the top of the great Tower and letting them gaze over the massed buildings of our city on the one hand and over the woods of Wytham and Blenheim on the other. I have devoted some thought to this problem, and I find the arguments nicely balanced. Let me briefly summarise them for you."

At this point Tennant felt that he must intervene.

"I'm sorry, Winn," he said, "I ought to have made my plan clearer to you. I'm sure we are all agreed that St. Thomas's has the primacy in Oxford for beauty as well as for other things. But it was in all our minds that the Senators would have to be shown everything in St. Thomas's, and most certainly under your personal guidance. I think, therefore, that for our choice of views for this evening we must all sign a self-denying ordinance and regard St. Thomas's as ineligible."

"Dear me," replied Winn, "that puts a different complexion on the whole matter. It seems a pity to deny these American gentlemen the best that we can offer, but, of course, I must submit to the editorial commands—provided, of course, that you can guarantee that they will be shown St. Thomas's properly before they leave."

"But certainly. Meantime I hope you will choose some other view to recommend to them."

Winn paused to rearrange his thoughts and then continued.

"I am, I confess, a traditionalist, and I am convinced that, especially in matters of taste, a judgment that has stood the test of time is almost sure to be correct. When succeeding generations have agreed that one particular view is the best in Oxford, they cannot surely be mistaken. So I must give my vote without hesitation to the High, with its wonderful curving sweep so much and so rightly admired. Then the Tower of Magdalen is beautifully placed, and Queen's and Univ. and All Souls give you an intoxicating promise of hidden beauties if you penetrate their gates. Yes, I'm sure I must vote for the High."

"What about the curve in Beaumont Street?" suggested Gresham. "Isn't that in a way more remarkable? Such a minute curve, and yet it turns what could otherwise be a dull and respectable thoroughfare into a thing of beauty."

"And what about the dimensions of Magdalen Tower?" asked Prendergast, who prided himself on his exact knowledge. "Do you know which sides of it are the broader—the north and south or the east and west? You can always tease a Magdalen man by asking him that question without prior notice."

Winn, however, was too much occupied with his own thoughts to consider these interruptions. "I'm not sure that I shall choose the High, after all," he announced; "for I've often thought that some of the approaches into Oxford must have been incomparably lovely in their day. Suppose we were living in 1820, could we see anything more serenely beautiful than the approach from Iffley towards Magdalen Bridge, as William Turner painted it? Or coming up the river towards Folly Bridge, or even nowadays the whole massive grandeur of Christ Church since the south side of the Hall was exposed to view? It must have been about 1924 or 1925 when enlightened men pulled down a lot of mean stables and houses and one saw that side of Christ Church as it had not been seen since the sixteenth century. But no, the whole range of Corpus and Merton, seen from the Meadows and across Deadman's Walk, is certainly finer. Dear me, this is really most difficult; I don't know what I ought to choose."

"What do you think of the approach to the City from the railway station?" enquired Pacey, not without malice.

"There is a story connected with that approach," answered Waterlow, "which, though no doubt apocryphal, is useful for the purpose of entertaining one's Cambridge friends. It goes like this. An Oxford man invited a Cambridge friend to visit him in order that he might see the sights. The Cambridge man accepted the invitation, full of hope that the beauties of Oxford would pale when compared with those of his own University, and anxious to minimise where he could the vaunted charms of the older University. He was met at the station and the two undergraduates drove in their hansom (yes, as you observe, it's an old story) towards the City and passed over the canal bridge. Here the Cambridge undergraduate, looking along the semi-stagnant branch of the canal, much, I fancy, in the manner in which the Queen of Sheba addressed King Solomon, turned to his friend and said grudgingly and unwillingly, 'Well, I must admit at least that your river is more beautiful than ours'."

"Do you know," said Winn, "I think I've changed my mind. Perhaps the views I mentioned just now are a little specialised. Would not the best view for the Senators be that wonderful one from the Upper Common Room at Queen's? I always used to tell young Fellows never in any circumstances to refuse an invitation to dine at Queen's, particularly in the summer, because they might then look down on such a wealth of great and historic buildings. It's a much more representative view, if that makes my meaning clear, than the others. It's there that I'd like to talk to the Senators rather than in the Bodleian quadrangle."

Once started on a topic, Winn was apt to continue for some time.

"I remember," he said, "how often in the war I used to

OXFORD IN WARTIME, from the painting by Paul Nash

meditate in that part of Oxford; for it appeared to me, when I read of the devastation caused by bombing from the air, that there was there in the centre of Oxford a most perilous concentration of the most precious buildings. Think of the Old Ashmolean and Bodley, the Divinity School and B.N.C., and the Radcliffe and All Souls and St. Mary's. The thought of the possible destruction of all that used to fill me with horror and keep me awake at nights. And then I began to speculate about the effects of a disaster of that kind, for it is often comforting to imagine the worst that is possible. My life, you know, has led me to indulge more in speculation than in action. Yes, I think I can say that speculation is my forte. But, let me see, where was I—I mustn't stray from my subject. Ah yes, I remember, it was wartime and I was speculating in the Bodleian quadrangle, and this is the problem which gradually shaped itself in my mind. England has two great ancient Universities—for the purpose of ready reference and to avoid any appearance of partiality, I will refer to them as Camford and Oxbridge, equal, or almost equal, in antiquity, in beauty, in tradition, and standing equally high in national esteem. No doubt you will readily guess to which Universities I refer and appreciate my little joke. Well, said I, let us suppose that the misfortune of war (for so I should regard it) led the enemy to launch a successful and devastating bombing attack on Camford, destroying beyond hope of repair all the ancient buildings of that noble city. Oxbridge, on the other hand, remained entirely unscathed. It needs no effort of imagination to understand that with the return of peace Camford would bend all its energies to the task of reconstruction. For a year or two, no doubt, it would be a place of desolation, but before long a new University would arise—not, however, the same University as of old. Of course, all the Colleges and the schools and libraries and galleries and museums would be rebuilt, but they would be rebuilt in the style of the mid-twentieth century—for the old order would have passed for ever. To an old fogey like myself no thought could be more horrible, but I should be compelled to admit that there would be certain compensatory advantages. Kitchens would be built contiguous to Halls, and with modern machinery to convey the food and crockery to and fro; every man would have an adequate number of cubic feet of space allotted to him for his living quarters; there would be labour-saving devices in every College, and running water in every bedroom and bathrooms on every staircase. I suppose that the number of servants would be reduced without increasing the amount of work expected from any. In short, you would have a new, a cheaper, and perhaps healthier University, paid for, as I suppose, by the War Damage Commission."

Trower for the first time displayed the liveliest interest.

"At a guess," he announced, "the expenses of each undergraduate would be reduced by at least twenty-five per cent., and repairs and renewals would diminish too. This is most interesting."

"Yes," said Winn, "so I thought. But remember that when Camford was destroyed Oxbridge remained unchanged. No doubt the immediate effect would be an immense gain for Oxbridge, but what would be the effect after, say, thirty years? That was the question which tormented me, and on which I speculated without reaching a conclusion for months on end. Of course for myself there could be only one answer. I would rather live in a fourteenth-century room and walk a quarter of a mile to the nearest bathroom than be housed in the most luxurious of modern apartments. But would others, and particularly younger folk, take the same view? After all, so much of the erstwhile Camford would remain—the traditions and the teachers and the communal life. And would a parent, perhaps in straitened circumstances, hesitate between a University which cost him three-quarters only of the sum which he must find to send a son to its rival? It's even possible that some of us old folk put too much emphasis on the importance of material things in the shape of fine buildings and treasured pictures. Why should not the things of the spirit flourish as well in rebuilt Camford as in ancient Oxbridge? So there I am with my problem unsolved. Which University would be the gainer at the end of thirty years? I hate to think that Camford might actually gain by this dreadful bombing, and yet I am forced to give due weight to the arguments which I have advanced on the other side. My mind turns, a little unwillingly, to Sir Christopher Wren and the rebuilding of London after the Great Fire. I look at the engraving which I have of London by Hollar of Prague before and immediately after the fire, I think of London rebuilt, and I speculate whether that visitation, in its day so awful, was not in reality a blessing. Dare I allow myself to think that the bombing of Camford could be a blessing too? A very, very difficult problem—Camford or Oxbridge? I hardly like to be dogmatic about the choice."

"It sounds to me like Stockton's story," said Tennant. "Which came out, the lady or the tiger? Frankly, Winn, I don't think that anyone can confidently answer the question you put—one way or another. I suspect that Trower and Pacey would cast their votes for the new model University and that Gresham and John and Mitton would be champions of Oxbridge, but I don't know. It seems to me, though, that it's a question on which the Senators might well be asked to pass judgment. I feel a little doubtful what view of Oxford you have finally chosen for them, but I'm sure that you have put forward an admirable topic for them to discuss, and I'm grateful to you for giving the views programme such a good start. Now, David, you assisted the side nobly last night; what view will you choose, and what argument will your choice provide?"

Prendergast made a faint protest on being called upon next, but he did not press his objection. "If your collaborators had a trade union, I should, in view of my efforts last night, not be allowed to work overtime to-day. Still, it may be an advantage to speak next, for Winn has appropriated so many views already that, if others follow his example, there will be nothing of real merit left for those who go in next. Personally I would reject all Winn's choices, and for this reason. To me the peculiar charm of Oxford views consists in the combination of buildings with natural objects; no one has ever really appreciated the University until he has stood in a College garden. Winn's street scenes have merit, no doubt, but he has forgotten the necessity for a garden as a background. I, therefore, have none of his doubts. Without the slightest hesitation I shall lead the Senators to my old College and let them feast their eyes on that paragon of all gardens. But they must see it in the right way and at the right time of day. Confident that we are in the vacation and that the Archery Club will not be meeting—for undergraduate arrows are apt to fly at a tangent—I shall lead them to the far end, forbidding them on pain of the fate of Lot's wife to look behind them until I give the word. And then I shall bid them turn round and gaze across the great expanse of grass to the noble building behind them. That I do aver is the finest view they will see here or in any other place. A building properly placed, and one which can be properly appreciated because of the great expanse of lawn which lies before it. Three-quarters of the great buildings of the world can never be seen as they should be because there is no view-point for the spectator."

"And what story will you attach to this view?" asked Tennant. "The Senators cannot fail to be impressed by your choice, but what story will you tell them, and what topic for discussion will you dangle, carrot-like, before their noses?"

"I shall tell them one simple story of the gardens, and one strange tale of the building, the first comparatively modern, the second of earlier days. At or about the turn of the century Mark Twain, then at the height of his fame, visited Oxford and the

University was full of tales of his wit and humour and of the brilliance of his conversation. The President of St. John's of that time enjoyed a reputation of the same kind, but he was growing old and he disliked publicity and self-advertisement. It seemed, therefore, that the dictates of good taste demanded that, if these two were to meet, the meeting should be of a private nature, so that the brisk interplay of epigram and reply should not deteriorate into an unworthy striving for verbal mastery. It was arranged, therefore, that Mark Twain should take a cup of afternoon tea with the President in the quiet privacy of the College Garden. To the Fellows, however, it seemed that such a plan might rob posterity of some memorable conversational bequest; perhaps, too, they were not without a natural curiosity. In any case, they determined that the interview should not pass without some record. You are to think of them, then, on that summer afternoon, concealed like the villains of a melodrama behind the arras —or, to speak plainly, lurking securely hid behind the bosky groves which border the great lawn; straining their ears to catch the *bons mots* which were to fall from the lips of the humorist or of the President. Here, they thought, are two of the cleverest men from two hemispheres—what may we not hear from them? Surely we can dine out on the treasured witticisms of this occasion for the next year or more! Mark Twain arrived and seated himself beside his host; there was a long pause, and the Fellows in their place of concealment hardly dared breathe. Finally, after deliberation, Mark Twain hazarded the remark that the weather was fine. The President considered this gambit and cautiously replied that he agreed but that he thought rain not improbable within the next few days. A promising start, but alas! a start only, for thereafter the silences became longer and neither man seemed able to keep the conversation at this high level—nothing, at least, beyond this opening gambit seemed worthy of record to the eager listeners."

"Do you think that story, though I don't question the moral lesson which it enforces, is really calculated to stimulate the conversational juices of the Senators?" asked Waterlow.

"That depends on their characters. If they are the men I think them, it will. If not, I shall pass rapidly to my account of the building of Laud's quadrangle. Laud was, I suppose, whatever we think of his churchmanship or his statesmanship, the greatest Oxonian of his day. Canterbury quadrangle was his own private gift to the College which he greatly loved; the building of it was started ten years after he had ceased to be President and completed when he had been Chancellor of the University for eight. Like other schemes of the kind, it developed from something comparatively modest into a grandiose undertaking. The final design left to St. John's what is, to my mind, the most graceful and perhaps the most pleasing quadrangle in Oxford. The munificence of Wolsey in an earlier age was matched by Laud, and the whole cost, which ran to something over five thousand pounds, was met by the Archbishop.

"What would that mean to-day?" enquired Trower.

"Precisely the question which, as I hope, one or other of the Senators will ask. I do not know the answer, but I feel sure that the erection and equipment of a similar building would hardly cost less than three or four hundred thousand. That will give me the opportunity of comparing the value of money then and now."

"I implore you not to engage the Senators in a discussion of the evils of inflation," protested Waterlow. "I, at any rate, have no claims to be an economist, and I don't want to acquire an inferiority complex *vis-à-vis* our guests."

"You need have no fear, for I shall hurry on to the more dramatic part of my tale. When Laud's building was finished, the King journeyed to Oxford to view the completed work. He was entertained to a prodigious feast in the New Library, and the following night Laud entertained the Heads of Houses and Uni-

versity officials to a second repast in the same place. What could
be more appropriate or more seemly? But the cost! There is no
record of the men who controlled the details of these feasts, but
the Trower of the day must, indeed, have surpassed himself, for
the cost of the entertainment appears to have been no less than
two thousand two hundred pounds, or about half the cost of the
quadrangle. Even American phlegm will be shaken by that
stupendous fact. How was it possible, even allowing for rich
presents and every conceivable luxury, to spend such a sum in
that time and for that purpose? I can well imagine a benefactor
of to-day giving, let us say, half a million to build a quadrangle,
of which (to quote the words of the Fellows of St. John's about
the Canterbury quadrangle) 'the very stones would give forth
music to his glory'. But I cannot, in the wildest flight of fancy,
imagine that that same benefactor would donate two hundred
and fifty thousand pounds to a dinner of celebration."

Gresham had shown visible signs of impatience while Prendergast was speaking, and he now intervened.

"Please, Tennant, may I claim the privilege of speaking next?
Thank you. Then I will tell you why I push myself forward,
though that, I hope, is not a malpractice of which I can often be
accused. The truth is that, whilst I agree with much of what
Prendergast has told us, I am wholly at variance with him on
certain points, and I want to discuss them before they are forgotten. Besides, I thought that I remarked a tendency on his part
to embark on the theory of benefactions, and that is a topic on
which I hold strong views. Let me, then, if I may, have the first
word on that."

"By all means," said Tennant, "but you must, I think, conform
to the arrangements on which we agreed. Each was to describe
his chosen view, and use that as a starting-point for discussion."

"Certainly, I shall not fail to observe the rules. I entirely accept
Prendergast's opinion that the peculiar charm of Oxford lies in

the blending of buildings with natural objects. Indeed, I would go further and say that the most perfect works of men's hands give the impression to the observer that they are, in fact, works of nature. If you look at the Taj Mahal, for example, either by moonlight or in the early morning, you feel (or at the least I have felt) that this can be no man-made edifice; **it is,** it must be, a thing of nature. Men are fond of comparing the tree trunks of the forest with the pillars of some vast cathedral—they would do better to compare the cathedral to the beauty of nature. That, I fancy, is what Heber felt when he wrote of the building of the Temple,

Like some tall palm the noiseless fabric sprung.

So far, so good—but I join issue with Prendergast when he advances his exaggerated claims for his old College. The view from St. John's Garden is beautiful, but there is something lacking. I opine that for scenic grandeur we must have mountains or else rugged cliffs or precipitous heights, and to them we cannot lay claim, but for sheer beauty of a gentler kind we must, to my thinking, have water. Beautiful buildings yes, beautiful trees and spacious lawns yes, but to them, and especially in the country of the Isis and the Cherwell, we must add water. And so, when my turn comes, I shall, after a lingering and half-regretful glance at Magdalen, lead the Senators to Worcester, and choose for them there my best-loved view. I shall take them to a point of vantage beyond the Lake, and let them gaze back to the proud mass of the eighteenth-century buildings and the Provost's Lodgings on the one hand and to the fifteenth-century Cottages on the other, with just a glimpse of the twentieth century behind. There, as it seems to me, and not at St. John's, you will find the best and loveliest of all Oxford views. And that thought leads me on to another. How is it that buildings so different in date and type and style harmonise so well? Go to Wadham and you will appreciate the beauty of a seventeenth-century College, which has remained unspoiled and indeed untouched. It is all of a piece, complete and in its own way perfect. At Worcester the beauty of the College is a beauty, not of unity or perfection— but of unexpected harmony. And always nature takes its part. Place a great copper beech between the buildings of the fifteenth century and those of the twentieth, and the two blend together as though they had been all part of one single plan. And the proud and indomitable eighteenth century falls into place too."

He paused and smiled. "And yet I have a book on my shelves, the title of which is *The Charm of Oxford*, and it makes no mention of Worcester."

Tennant interrupted him. "Don't let us put forward the views we admire much as though this was a sort of competition for the Senators. They shall see them all and American appreciation should be wide enough to embrace them all. But you've not carried out yet the other part of your task. Remember that the chosen view was to be only the starting-point of some subject of discussion with them. What are you going to tell the Senators when you show them this favourite view of yours?"

Gresham did not hesitate. "I shall tell them in a few brief words the history of the College, because I think nothing else will make the Oxford scene so vivid to them as the history of some one—I had almost said any one—college. The changes of fortune, the alternations of prosperity and decay! It will make the task of describing the College system much easier. May I do that?"

Winn interrupted him. "Are you sure that your account will be historically accurate and true?" he asked. (4)

"Not true in the sense that your history of St. Thomas's will be true," Gresham replied; "but essentially true all the same. It will be guide-book history of a superior type. I've no patience with your scientific historians. The best history is like the art of Rembrandt; it throws a vivid light on certain selected causes and leaves the rest in shadow or unseen. I think that's a quotation, but I'm not sure—anyhow, it's the truth. Sometimes I fancy that one could go further. Don't we get a picture of a past age which is nearer the truth from novels and plays or even violently one-sided pamphlets than we do from the most impartial and cautious and learned works of research? Especially I think when we love the men and the places about which we speak, for charity, as my tutor used to tell me, is a great illuminant. But let me try my prentice hand and Winn will stop me if I stray too far from the historical facts."

Winn shook his head. Towards Gresham he was always less critical and more sympathetic than towards his other colleagues, for he recognised a kindred spirit.

"Very well then," Gresham proceeded. "Worcester, under the name of Gloucester College, was founded by Sir John Giffard towards the end of the thirteenth century. It was a Benedictine foundation, and the abbeys and monasteries established each its own house or camera to which chosen novices were sent to study and to earn a degree. I shall point out to the Senators the row of cameræ on the south side of the quadrangle, patched and changed and repaired and weather-beaten, but still essentially what they were at the time of their first construction. I have no gift of description, but I shall say to them that, to the best of my belief, undergraduates have lived and worked there for the better part of six centuries. University and Balliol and Merton may be older, but have they many or any rooms of which that can be said? I shall refrain, I think, from pointing out the excellences of that hard grey stone which has outlived its yellower brother of a later age. I'm sorry—I mustn't digress too much. It's the continuous and intimate College life which impresses me—more than the material survival. Do you remember that eloquent passage in Mallet's *History of the University* when, speaking of another quadrangle, and musing on the religious changes which it had seen, he says: 'To-day the heirs of Wolsey's great foundation, visibly secular and superbly young, possess the place where the Black Monks of Canterbury dwelt, and pay their shy and intermittent homage to the old ideals of study and of prayer.' That pleases me, and I speculate not on the differences but on the similarities of the Benedictine novice and, let us say, the Rhodes Scholar of to-day."(5)

Tennant's eyebrows hinted a mild reproof.

"Forgive me," Gresham went on. "I know that I must not digress too much. Gloucester College flourished and, as I think, contributed its share to true religion and sound learning—and its share also to the life of Oxford. Sometimes, I suppose, there were a hundred or more undergraduates within the walls. Then came the dissolution of the monasteries, and the dissolution, too, of Gloucester College. It fell into the hands of the King, it was for a time a Bishop's palace, it drifted into private ownership. But old ideas die hard, and as Gloucester Hall it continued to be a home for a varying number of students and other persons, many of the Catholic persuasion. I am tempted, sorely tempted, to dally over the history of the Hall, but Tennant would not allow me to do so—instead, I move forward to the end of the seventeenth century, and I look at Loggan's print of 1683. The remains of a Chapel and a Hall and a Library, crumbling walls and half-decayed buildings; the end is in sight. A few undergraduates still come from time to time to shelter themselves in those rooms which remain habitable; a few families have settled or squatted among the ruins; the Principal is still housed on the north side of the old quadrangle. Life goes on, but still surely the end is in sight—soon Gloucester Hall will be a memory, just as its former neighbours, Oseney Abbey and Beaumont Palace, are already memories! Fortunately the event was otherwise. Benjamin Woodroffe, who became Principal in 1692, was a disgruntled crank, but he was at least a man of ideas, and he set himself to revive the failing fortunes of his Hall. His first experiment was hardly a success. In an attempt to reunite the Church of England and the Orthodox Church, he turned Gloucester Hall into a Greek College and summoned his undergraduates from Constantinople. Alas! the Orthodoxy of the newcomers was not proof against vacation visits to the continent of Europe; Woodroffe was soon engaged in litigation with his peccant undergraduates, and his academic life was interrupted by visits to the Fleet Prison. Then another vista of hope opened up. Sir Thomas Cookes, baronet of Worcestershire, is the new character who steps onto the stage in my drama—for drama it is. He was a wealthy man and he let it be known that he proposed to leave at his death a sum of some £10,000 to found a new College or to embellish some already existing ornamental pile. In the Library you can still see an oil painting of Cookes in an attitude of veneration before a bust of King Alfred, the reputed founder of the earliest Oxford College. The figure, judging from the picture in the Hall, is not a portrait, and by all the accepted canons of art the work is lamentable, but the purpose is surely impeccable.

"To Woodroffe, as rich in projects as he was poor in resources, the bait was irresistible. If Gloucester Hall was not an already existing ornamental pile, then words had lost their meaning; if it did not need embellishment, then Loggan was no artist. He fell upon Cookes; he drew up statutes for a new Worcester College; he lived in a golden haze of fellowships and endowments and new buildings and undergraduates of birth and fortune. 'Hopeful sprouts' as perhaps he called them. But the bait attracted other fish than him; other colleges, even if they could not be newly founded, could well claim to be embellished. One after another made its effort to obtain the spoil. From Balliol the Senior Fellow (or was it the Master?) journeyed to Worcestershire with a letter and with a sermon to be preached to the moribund baronet. In the letter it was remarked—a queer mixture of truth and falsehood—that it was not generally known that the links between Balliol and Worcestershire were so strong that Balliol was commonly known as 'Worcester College' in the University of Oxford. That I suppose was the most critical moment in the history of my College, but the danger passed. Sir Thomas Cookes died and the money was still unappropriated; our so-called founder did not mention the College in his will, nor indeed leave it a penny. By a merciful intervention of Providence, Woodroffe died also and a new Principal was appointed in his place, a man who, owing to his love of a glass, was not unnaturally well seen in the Oxford society of that day. Meantime the lawyers began to take a hand, and the Court of Chancery occupied itself with the claims and counter-claims of the rival applicants. The court was propitious and Worcester College was incorporated by Royal Charter—I think that is the expression—two days before the death of Queen Anne."

"Well," said Tennant, "it's an interesting tale and I see no reason why it should not figure in the guide-book, but what exactly do you wish it to convey to the Senators?"

"It appears to me that the life of a College, or indeed of any institution, is curiously like the life of an individual, with its times of success and failure, of prosperity and poverty, of sickness and health. And every College does have a personality or rather perhaps an ethos of its own. What I want to give the Senators is a brief history of one College, because I think that will help them to appreciate the chequered histories of all the rest."

"I agree," said Tennant; "but there's something else. You cannot very well discuss this with them. They will just agree with you and the rest is silence. What topic of disagreement will you dangle before them? How will you stimulate the senatorial mental processes?"

Gresham hesitated. "I'm really not quite sure," he replied. "If Porson (or Samson, for that matter) turns out to be a Victorian sentimentalist—as he well may do—I shall read him Burgon's poem on Worcester and invite him to consider the ethical value of sentimental attachment. (6) But, no, I need a more general topic. I think it shall be the theory of benefactions, for there is no College in Oxford which does not owe much or all to its benefactors. I shall suggest that the generally accepted theory that the day of benefactors has passed is quite erroneous."

"Hasn't it?" enquired Pacey.

"Not at all, but the method has changed. The old plan was to devise a large sum by will, thereby no doubt allaying all pricks of conscience. It always seemed to me that the testator had little personal satisfaction from his generosity. Consider Worcester again for a moment. George Clarke, who was Member for the University and the friend of Dean Aldrich, surely did much more for the College than its founder. He gave money and he left books in his will, he planned and started the construction of new buildings—in a way, he adopted the College and launched it on its new career. True, he left much for it in his will, but on balance he must most have enjoyed what he did during his lifetime. The great modern benefactors have done their good deeds whilst they could themselves see something of the results."

"And escape death duties," hazarded Prendergast.

"Certainly, and escape death duties. I yield to no one in my dislike of death duties, which I think run counter to social justice, but I do admit that they may encourage benefactions. That is a point which may appeal to Aristotle."

"I think, if I rightly apprehend the sort of mind which Aristotle has, that he will ask you a question at that point," said Tennant, "and I think it will run something like this. 'Mr. Gresham,' he will say, 'I am profoundly impressed by your devotion to your College or institution—a feeling, I may say, which is highly regarded in the United States of America. Now tell me, Sir, if some public-spirited citizen were to approach you and announce his intention of donating a very large sum to your University, to what purpose would you advise him to devote his money?' How would you answer that?"

"I should have no hesitation at all, for I should mount at once my favourite hobby-horse. How often have I enjoyed in imagination the luxury of spending a million for the benefit of others! My firm conviction is that nowadays too much is done for the young and far too little for the old. I believe, perhaps we all believe, that no one should be prevented from coming to the University by lack of money, or, in other words, that everyone worthy of a University education should receive it. But are we not in danger of making it rather *too* easy for anyone to acquire sufficient money from the State or from some local authority—to acquire, I mean, enough money to pay all his expenses here? There is a type of young man who thinks that he is suffering a social injustice if, having once passed the Higher School Certificate, he is not maintained in term and vacation for the period of his academic life."

"And he's right, isn't he, if he thinks that?" said Pacey, a little truculently.

"I don't think so. In the past, no doubt, many men came up here because their parents had money and it was socially advantageous to have been at Oxford, but, none the less, a great number came, and could only come, because they had won open scholarships, and even then their parents had to make sacrifices to find the additional money which was needed. It ought to be difficult and not easy for men to come to the University; nothing that can be had too easily is ultimately worth having."

"We are back again at our central problem," said Pacey. "Why do men wish to come here, and how should we choose those who are to come? For my part, I would have an open competitive examination for all candidates which was common to all Colleges."

"And I, once again, in my capacity as chairman," objected Tennant, "must rule that that particular problem must be postponed till a later session. The word is with Gresham, who is, in his own words, still mounted on his hobby-horse."

"Perhaps it was my fault," said Gresham placably. "I intended only to make the point that, on the whole, the young have nowadays ample opportunities. Probably I ought to have pointed not to entrance here but to the 'post-graduate' grants and the fellowships and lectureships for young researchers. Isn't it true, Pacey, that a young scientist can get a grant tolerably easily to carry on his research, whether it comes from the State or from a business firm or from a University?"

"Only if he is a good scientist," retorted Pacey. "And again only because the supply of good scientists is far below the demand in the modern world."

"Well, I won't argue about that, for my concern is not with the young but with the old—not with the recruit but with the veteran—and when I consider the case of those who reach the retiring age I seem to see not only an element of tragedy but a shameful waste of man-power."

"Few scientists do really first-class or original work after they are forty," objected Pacey.

"Then I must confine my remarks to the veterans of the Arts subjects," replied Gresham, thus adroitly cutting Pacey out of the argument. "This is the picture that I see: a teacher of languages, a professor of history, a College tutor in philosophy arrives at the age of sixty-five; his appointment ends—his pension, which thirty years before had appeared in prospect almost riches, is now, after the fall in the value of money, inadequate. He retires to some provincial or suburban dwelling and the world knows him no more. That is where my benefactor comes in! He will found a College which dons can go to when they retire, and live happily ever, or almost ever, afterwards."

"An intellectual almshouse," commented Prendergast.

"I think you are a Socialist at heart, after all," said Pacey with a rather sour smile.

Gresham was not easy to provoke.

"I will cheerfully submit to be called a Socialist if I can get my College," he replied, "but I've not explained yet what I think it could be. Let me be more explicit. In the first place, we have never found the modern substitute for the country living; when all dons were in Holy Orders they retired as a matter of course to a College living for their latter years. But now! For the most part they have nowhere to go and nothing to do, or rather nothing which they can do away from their natural milieu. Yet what might they not do if given the necessary encouragement! I believe that the doctors would tell you that most men deteriorate in the late sixties or early seventies, but that doesn't mean that they are good for nothing. Think of a Professor of Modern History retiring at sixty-five. How often is there a book half written, a line of research laid aside for the leisure that has never come. And think, too, of the use that he could be to younger historians; a retired professor ought to be a great book of reference, and a book not laid aside on a dusty shelf in Wimbledon or Torquay but open on the table of my new College. It's sad to think how much knowledge and experience disappears when a really learned man dies—you don't want to bury him prematurely as well. Who was the patron saint of the old, Mitton?"

"I'm not sure; indeed I doubt if there was one," replied the Chaplain.

"Very well then, if such a saint can be found, my College shall be named after him."

"I never thought of you as a reformer, Gresham," said Prendergast, "and I'm delighted to see you in a new rôle, but still I say 'intellectual almshouse'."

"I really don't think so, provided only that the College is started in the right way. Let fellowships be considered as the highest intellectual honour which the old can receive, just as an All Souls Fellowship is the supreme prize for the young. As I see it, there will be twenty or twenty-five Fellows in all, each with his own set of rooms. They'll draw no emoluments, but they'll have their rooms and their communal dinner and really good service—and they'll go on living the communal life that they have learned to like ["I knew you were a Socialist"—from Pacey] within reach of the best of libraries and in touch with all the intellectual interests of Oxford. Imagine the thrill for a young don—or even a young scholar—of being invited to dine at St. Nemo's and making contact with the best minds of the generation before his own. What intellectual enterprises might not originate from such evenings, what books might not be written in the St. Martin's Summer of a Fellow of St. Nemo's! The more I contemplate my plan, the more it commends itself to me."

"How would you choose your Fellows?" enquired Prendergast.

"No doubt the first Fellows would have to be nominated, but once established the College would be self-governing, and the Fellows would themselves elect when vacancies occurred. I think the right period would be ten years, with a possible prolongation for five years more."

"But you couldn't put the poor old creatures into the street at eighty," exclaimed Prendergast.

"Firstly they are not poor old creatures, and secondly I think you could. For consider—they will have had fifteen happy and useful years which otherwise they would have missed; their savings will by then be considerable, and in many cases they will wish to end their days in a nursing-home or among their relatives. But I don't know, perhaps there ought to be a seniors' wing to the building—I'll think about that."

"Will there be married quarters?" asked Prendergast, who was now giving the whole of his attention to the matter under discussion.

"Well, that is a difficult point," Gresham admitted. "I confess that I am uncertain . . ."

It was Winn, hitherto silent, who entered the discussion at this point. "My dear Gresham," he said with a courteous inclination of his head, "your project does credit to your humanity (not that I should ever question that), and is, in my estimation, both beneficent and practicable, but I must implore you not to jeopardise its success by any vacillation on this important issue. Of course you must not have women in your college. Nobody thought of women playing any part in University life when I was an undergraduate; I really do not think that there *were* women in Oxford—certainly it never occurred to us to miss them. Let me see, though, they used to come to Eights Week, and everyone was very pleased to see them. But that of course was a special occasion. No, emphatically, I cannot consent to the admission of women to St. Nemo's."

"Shades of Queen Victoria!" murmured Pacey.

"Then that is satisfactorily settled," said Prendergast. "It only remains for Gresham to find some childless millionaire with a soft heart for his scheme to be completed."

"If I do find him," said Gresham, "and persuade him to endow the College, he will do more for education and learning than any benefactor has done yet."

Tennant would hardly have allowed any other of his colleagues, except perhaps Winn, to have spoken so long without interruption. He now felt it time to intervene.

"I like your plan, Gresham, just as Winn does, but I am a little doubtful of its utility for purely guide-book purposes. We can hardly expect the Senators to shower their wealth on Oxford when they have only been here for twenty-four hours."

"Good heavens, no; I had no intention of trying to extort money from our guests. It does appear to me, though, that this sort of discussion can be fruitful when, for example, we show them Nuffield College, or All Souls, or St. Antony's."

"I'll admit that," Tennant replied, "and I'm sure that we can all agree that Gresham has contributed his full quota to the evening's symposium. Now, Chaplain, it's your turn. What is your favourite view?"

"If you'll allow me," said Mitton, "I will first collect a short note which I wrote a few days ago about one of the sights of Oxford. It would, I feel sure, be appropriate and useful for the guide-book."

"To leave an Oxford Common Room when your companions remain argues either a thick skin or great confidence in the integrity of your personal character," said Prendergast.

"Or both," suggested Waterlow with a glance at Mitton's empty chair. "But whatever will his chosen view be?"

"Surely," said Tennant, "we should be able to guess. Our Chaplain, to use the expression which he would himself employ, is indeed the salt of the earth, but even his best friends would agree that he is extremely conventional, and consequently that his actions, opinions, and indeed his expressions are predictable in advance. He will certainly choose some view which has a religious significance and which gives him furiously to think. He will also find a view which enables him to enforce some orthodox moral lesson."

"Let's have a sweepstake with half-crown antes," suggested Trower. "Come on, everyone must be in, and we'll choose a subject for him in turn. And if anyone pretends that he hasn't got a half-crown, I can provide change. Come on, Pacey, you are junior and this is court-martial procedure; what's your fancy?"

Pacey rather unwillingly produced half a crown and placed it on the table.

"He will select St. Mary's," he stated with decision, "and he'll describe to the Senators the moving scene of a University Sermon. The money's mine already."

"No, no, no," exclaimed Winn, who had with some difficulty discovered two threepenny bits, a shilling, and a couple of sixpences. "Mitton is a loyal and devoted college man, and, since you will not permit him to mention St. Thomas's, he will surely lead the Senators to his old College. I cast my vote for Keble."

"Wrong again," said Tennant. "Mitton will indubitably settle upon the Martyrs' Memorial, the standing symbol of Protestant triumph."

"He will do nothing of the sort," retorted Prendergast, "because he will be afraid of being asked why the undergraduates climb it. I seem to remember that he ran into very troubled water when he preached on that topic last term. I was left wondering whether 'the natural and laudable bent of headstrong and temerarious youth towards acts of peril and adventure' was to be allowed to weigh in the balance against those wanton, even childish displays of bad taste which offend Christian sentiment and bring a tear to the cheek of age and experience'. Of course he won't choose the Martyrs' Memorial. It's the Cathedral that will win—the perfect example of the marriage between religion and education, reminding us all——"

"Stop," said Trower, "we haven't much time, and your half-crown's on the Cathedral. Next, please."

"In my opinion," said Waterlow, "you underrate the Chaplain's genuine religious feeling. I agree that he will choose something to illustrate the fact, which he feels strongly, that Oxford is a place both of religion and education, but I don't think that he will choose the Cathedral for that. I remember how shocked he was when I told him that Christ Church undergraduates were never allowed to button their surplices because that would enable them to conceal their riding breeches."

"I've known College chapels where exceptionally roomy trousers were used to disguise deficiencies of toilet," said Prendergast. "Isn't that the true origin of 'Oxford Bags', John?"

"I don't know, but I do feel sure that Mitton will choose a simple College chapel, but I don't know which. May I put my money on 'a College chapel', or let us say 'the interior of a College chapel'?"

"Yes," said Trower, "that's fair enough, though you'll have to go halves with Winn if he chooses Keble Chapel, provided that you ante up, which you haven't yet done. Thank you. Now, Gresham."

"I think you are all mistaken," said Gresham. "Mitton will wish not only to bring the religious side of Oxford life vividly before the eyes of the Senators, but also to show them how broad-minded he is. Beauty and music must play their part in our devotion as well as dogma and ritual—you've all heard him say that. Without the slightest doubt he will conduct the Senators to the top of Magdalen Tower—in imagination I mean—and there give them a highly coloured account of May morning."

"There doesn't seem much left for me," said Trower, as he added his coin to the pile. "Let me see, seventeen and six in the kitty, that's right, and I'm surprised it is. Well, all the favourites have been backed, but I've seen many good things down the course in my day, so I shall back the field. It isn't an awfully good bet, but I'm not without hope. Hullo, there he is coming back."

Holding a small note-book in his hand, Mitton took his seat again at the table, and addressed his companions.

"Whilst some of you have been speaking," he began, "I have been giving earnest attention to the choice before me—indeed, I may confess quite frankly that this difficult choice has given me furiously to think. What, I ask myself, is the view in Oxford which has given me most satisfaction, and which has moved and stimulated me most? What, I ask again, is the view which will

mean most to the receptive minds of our most welcome transatlantic visitors?"

Mitton paused and looked round the table. The tense interest
displayed by his hearers, to which he was unaccustomed, seemed
to afford him gratification.

"That choice may mean much to them, and I own that the
longer I consider it the more difficult does it appear. What view
shall I choose? Certainly not one of the more obvious or hack-
neyed; only a shallow mind would lead our visitors to the view
of the High [Winn winced slightly] or to Tom Quad. They are
beautiful, but not, I think, instructive. I must make a more
original, a more worth-while choice than that, something at once
more characteristic of Oxford and more apt to impress the
Senators with the value of Oxford life. And so, piercing below
the surface of things, I observe that the most important, and the
most often forgotten, truth about this beautiful city is that it is
not only a place of learning but also a centre of true religion.
What view, then, will impress that truth firmly on our visitors'
minds?"

"Yes, what view?" asked three of the listeners at the same time.

Palpably flattered by the interest taken in his address, but
unwilling to be hurried, Mitton continued:

"Naturally," he said, "my mind turned instinctively to St.
Mary's, the centre of our University religious life, our University
Church."

A smile of self-satisfaction appeared on Pacey's face, but his
companions were not disposed to allow him so easy a victory.

"Don't you think that some of those bosses in the interior are
really out of keeping with a Christian church—that one of
Gandhi for example?" enquired Prendergast.

"I recall to mind," added Waterlow, "that when Gandhi
visited Oxford and stayed at one of our ancient Colleges, the
Master let it be known that he would dine in Hall on one of the

evenings of his visit. Gandhi, I must remind you, did not enjoy a universal popularity at that time, and his habitual dress would not have commended itself to Mr. Gladstone."

"Why Mr. Gladstone?" enquired Pacey.

"Because Mr. Gladstone when pressed to describe the changes at Oxford between the time of his own youth and his old age was passionately moved by the deterioration in the dress of under-graduates. But to continue—a rather nervous Oxford tailor asked for an appointment with the Master of that College and told him that he felt that the Master should know that he, the tailor, had received an order for one hundred loin-cloths. I've never quite forgiven that tailor—why couldn't he hold his tongue? A cap and gown—especially a Commoner's gown—and a loin-cloth would be a curious costume, but it would surely conform to the definition of academic dress. Alas! Gandhi dined privately with the Master."

Mitton turned rather red in the face. "I regard that as a most indecent story, Waterlow, and one which I am quite sure you have invented. I trust that you will in no circumstances relate it to the Senators. For myself, I shall try to forget it and continue my account of my own cogitations. I decided, regretfully, that I should *not* choose St. Mary's because, great though its influence for good is, it yet plays, as I think, less part in the daily life of the University than some other religious edifices."

Like an errant butterfly the smile left Pacey's face and settled instead on the faces of Winn and Waterlow.

"Keble, my old college, flashed into my mind."

"What better choice," murmured Winn, who had entered with elderly enthusiasm into the spirit of the game. "I have always maintained that Keble is beautiful; you should view it on a dark night from the Parks—you can't see those hideous polychromatic bricks and the great mass of the buildings stands out like a great Rock of Gibraltar. Of course that's the view to show them. I forgot, though, that the view from the Parks is partly spoilt since they built the new Clarendon Laboratory—another of the attacks of Science on Beauty."

"Do you know I am tempted to agree with you," said Waterlow. "Architecturally Keble does represent the taste of the time, and it's not just a slavish copy. That taste in buildings will come full circle is almost certain. I fancy that foreign architects would prefer Keble to many of the copied buildings which the generality of people now admire. But why not take them to Keble Chapel? After all, that is the centre of the College and the *Light of the World* is a great picture. Would not the Pre-Raphaelites suit the taste of the Senators? And a College chapel is just what you ought to show them."

A whisper of "Shame" from Prendergast was stifled by Mitton's next remark.

"I yield to no one in my love for Keble and my admiration of its spirit," he said, "but I feel it is not exactly what I am looking for. For one thing, it lacks antiquity; the spiritual value of association is very strong, and it grows stronger with the years. Thinking thus, another, and a nobler, prospect passed through my mind. I seemed to have found the ideal choice."

"Magdalen Tower?" suggested Gresham.

"Oh no, something much more simple, yet to me much more impressive. That plain bronze cross on the ground at the west end of the Broad, the cross that marks the spot where the Protestant Martyrs met their end. Think of Cranmer at the end of his series of hesitations and recantations plunging his hand into the hottest part of the fire; think of the gallant Latimer and the stout Ridley. What better subject with which to enthral the Senators, or what better subject to point a moral and adorn a tale?"

Winn and Pacey, whose half-crowns were already irremediably lost, could afford to chuckle, but consternation reigned among the rest.

"Surely that would be an unwise choice," Prendergast objected. "The Senators we know to be acute and curious men. They will immediately ask whether the twentieth century can match the sixteenth in the fervour of its religious belief. Depend upon it, they will ask you, Mitton, if you would go to the stake for your faith and if you would behave with the same cool courage—no, how stupid of me, cool is quite the wrong word—with the same fervent daring as the martyrs."

"I hope that in similar embarrassing circumstances I should do nothing unbecoming my cloth," said Mitton, a little stiffly.

"You would hardly be a free agent," retorted Prendergast.

Tennant rallied to his support. "There are other objections, Mitton, which I feel sure you have overlooked. All Senators are photogenic and most certainly Porson and Samson and Aristotle will expect, and indeed demand, to be photographed at each historic spot. Now you cannot be photographed in the Broad. That would be vulgar advertisement; besides, the façade of Balliol would be an impossible background. I implore you not to commit so gross an error of taste. If you wish to speak of the Protestant Martyrs—and you could choose no better theme—why not assemble your party at the Martyrs' Memorial and tell them its history and significance?"

It is doubtful whether Mitton appreciated the murmurs of "Objection" which arose; it is certain that Trower's crisp announcement that the Stewards would disqualify Tennant's horse and warn him off for the rest of the season meant nothing to him. He was, however, disinclined to accept Tennant's suggestion.

"In point of fact," he said, "I decided after some thought not to speak of the Martyrs at all, for it seemed to me that that choice would be a little stereotyped. I needed something more original, and so I decided quite definitely to show them the stained glass and the War Memorial in New College Chapel."

Prendergast, as a lawyer, knew that no cause was irremediably lost until the verdict had been officially delivered, and he made a last effort.

"Stained glass—of course that is right, but why not go to the Cathedral? I admit that there is little glass there of merit, but at one time the whole place was full of seventeenth-century glass—Van Linge, I think. The Chapter decided to change it all, but the undergraduates petitioned that one window, the Jonah window, might remain, and they carried their point. It's still there at the west end. To me that's a fine example of the instinctive good taste of the young, though I dare say it was the subject rather than the artistic merit of the window which saved Jonah. There's an agreeable little whale in the background and a handsome gourd beside the prophet."

But Mitton shook his head.

"No, I prefer New College. Besides, by a curious coincidence I had the great good fortune to be shown round New College Chapel by the Warden only last week, and I made a little note of the story which he told me. It looks as though Providence had foreseen that I should be asked to contribute to a guide-book."

Trower's hand strayed towards the little pile of silver on the table. "I announce," he said with ponderous jocularity, "that Major Trower is the winner of the July sweepstake. Providence sometimes arranges that outsiders should win or there would be no betting. I always feel that Providence is really on the side of the punter."

Deep in his note-book Mitton failed to take up the challenge. Instead he began his account of the New College windows.

"I shall not take you back to the beginning," he said, "but start with the eighteenth century—a great period of restoration and experiment in New College Chapel, which had, of course, originally been filled with the ancient glass which dated back to the time of the founder. In 1745 Price had finished his so-called restoration of the south windows of the Chapel.

In effect they were all new glass and clearly eighteenth century in manner. The College were so much pleased that they decided to go on with the replacement of the ancient glass in the Chapel with glass in the modern manner. In 1765 Peckitt took out the large Jesse window in the west wall of the Antechapel and replaced it with his own glass. The College were dissatisfied both with the colour and the drawing and told him so, but nevertheless paid the bill. In 1773 he was surprised to find that he was asked to do more windows for the College, but he was told that it was on condition that he did not draw or paint the windows himself. Biagio Rebecca was chosen to do the work, and he completed the three west windows on the north side of the Chapel itself. At the end of the decade, while Rebecca was on the work, Peckitt was told that the College had at last decided to get a really good window by the greatest artist of the time installed in the Antechapel in place of Peckitt's work. This, of course, referred to the employment of Reynolds, and Peckitt was told to take out his window. He imagined, doubtless, that it would be destroyed, but a little later he was told that the College had spent so much money that it was necessary to call off Biagio Rebecca before he completed the windows at the east end of the north side of the Chapel, and Peckitt's glass from the west window should be kept. At some subsequent date, when the medieval glass was taken out of the remaining two windows at the east end, Peckitt's glass was put in its place. This time it had to be cut down, since the lights of the Chapel were rather narrower than the lights of the great west window. His signature, therefore, appears at the right-hand bottom corner of the window nearest the east end in the form 'W. $\frac{Peck}{Pin}$'."

"Thank you," said Tennant. "That is all of interest to me, and will, I am sure, be of interest to the Senators also; but I should like to know just what subject for discussion you are hoping to raise with them."

In New College Chapel

"I hope," replied Mitton optimistically, "to introduce at least three topics. In the first place I shall draw attention to the, apparently, inevitable cycle of taste in artistic matters. Did not Ruskin say that, whatever else was said of it, no one would ever venture to deny that the Meadow Buildings at Christ Church were beautiful? In the second place, I shall discuss the function of stained glass in places of worship. Æsthetically I am myself deeply impressed by the beauty of the Reynolds window, yet I often feel that the older glass produces a deeper feeling of reverence and devotion. Is it not true that one of the best-known eulogies in the eighteenth century of the New College glass was really applied to Peckitt's window which many preferred to Reynolds's? And thirdly I want to draw their attention to the character of Peckitt. It seems to me that he must have been a man of unusual beauty of character; no snub, no natural feeling of pique aroused by the removal of his window, no false pride about the employment of another artist to draw and paint his windows prevented him from doing his utmost for the embellishment of the Chapel. I think of working a little reference to him and his history into my sermon on humility. It is a sermon which always appeals to the young men. Oh! and I almost forgot the most important part of my talk. I mean to show them—or at least Porson and Aristotle—for I fear that I may be over Samson's head—how well the Church of England knows how to lay art and music, colour and sound, under contribution to aid and foster feelings of devotion. ["May morning on Magdalen Tower," murmured Gresham regretfully.] I want them to realise as they stand in the Chapel how closely knit are religion and education and how truly Oxford is the home of both."

Tennant interrupted him before the Chaplain could enlarge further on his favourite topic.

"I thought you had it in mind," he said, "to speak also about the War Memorial in New College Chapel—or rather in the Antechapel. Or was I mistaken?"

"Yes, indeed," replied Mitton, "and in some ways I feel that that will be the most valuable part of my talk to the Senators. I want to show them first the War Memorial to the fallen of the 1914–19 war, and then beside it the tablet which commemorates the German Rhodes Scholars who fell in the same struggle, fighting on the other side.

> In memory of the men of this College who coming from a Foreign Land entered into the inheritance of this place and Returning fought and died for their country in the war 1914–1919
> Prinz Wolrad-Friedrich zu Waldeck-Pyrmont
> Freiherr Wilhelm von Sell: Erwin Beit von Speyer

To me it seems that the erection of that tablet is a truly Christian act of commemoration."

Prendergast demurred. "At the time," he said, "there was considerable criticism. A great many people thought that it was wrong, that it would give offence to many relatives of the fallen, and that it was an act of misplaced sentimentality."

Winn interrupted with unusual vigour. "It cannot have been wrong," he exclaimed. "I have myself heard two strangers confessing with reverence that, in their opinion, no other country would have been capable of an act of such magnanimity. No, no; it cannot be wrong to forgive our enemies when the struggle is over, or to accord our tribute of respect to those who have done their duty according to their lights. I can well see that a commemorative tablet of this kind might be called in question in many places, but surely not in Oxford, which is the home of freedom and liberality of thought."

Prendergast smiled a little grimly.

"My dear Winn," he said, "your sentiments do you credit, but tell me truly what would have been your own attitude in 1920 towards a proposal to commemorate German Rhodes Scholars in St. Thomas's Chapel? I put it to you that you would have said that the proposal might give offence to many well-meaning persons, that it was a mistake to stir up unnecessary controversy, and that it would be wiser to postpone any action till the years had brought gentler feelings?"

A real personal humility was one of the endearing traits in Winn's character. He had, too, more self-understanding than most men.

"You are right to correct me, Prendergast," he admitted. "I fear that my natural timidity would have constrained me to act precisely in the manner you have described. Dear me, it is humiliating to realise how little moral courage one has! But now that I can view the matter dispassionately I am convinced that those liberal-minded men at New College were wholly right, and I regret that St. Thomas's has no similar memorial. I am becoming a foolish and forgetful old man, but I can still appreciate courage and decision in others. I am inclined to think that that New College memorial, whatever was said at the time, is a credit to the whole University."

Prendergast seemed ready to contest the point, but Tennant stopped him. "It's pretty late," he said, "for these views have taken longer to describe than I expected. I think we ought to adjourn till to-morrow, and that John Waterlow ought to say his piece first then."

CHAPTER IV

"Have any of you considered," began the Hon. John Water-low, "that the sun shone upon us to-day just as it blazed down yesterday and the day before? And have you proceeded further in your meditations to consider, as I have, that in spite of the persistence, the invariability of an English climate—for as St. Swithin told us long ago it is the unchanging perseverance of the English climate in good or ill that is its chief characteristic —it *is* within the bounds of possibility even if it is improbable that next week we may have rain?"

"No," said Trower. "I am not an imaginative man."

"But, I, thank God, am. Think, then, of these unfortunate Senators standing beneath their dripping umbrellas in the Bodleian quadrangle whilst David harangues them on the constitution of the University; think of them padding over the wet pavements in Mitton's train to New College; think of them peering through the deluge to admire the curve of the High; think of them, above all, among the sodden bamboos by the Lake at Worcester hanging with wet but bated breath on Gresham's words, as he elaborates his theory that no view can have merit unless it includes water! Ancient buildings, however beautiful, demand sunshine; what can be more lugubrious than damp and sweating stone? And new buildings too. Go to Lady Margaret Hall and observe the Chapel when the sun is shining on it; in a moment you are transported to Spain or Italy and all the sunshine of the Mediterranean creeps into your veins (just as at night if you walk down Brasenose Lane or Bear Street you may think yourself in the Florence of the fifteenth century). Besides, has any one of you even considered for a moment that one of the Senators may come from Florida! Think of that, and tremble! The statistics of sunshine in Florida over the last fifty years is a formidable and envy-provoking subject; handled by Aristotle, it will leave little time for Winn's account of the Parliament of 1681 or Mitton's narrative of the last hours of Cranmer. Indeed, with a horrid certainty I see the guide-book trembling on the verge of disaster. Maybe, though, I can save it yet."

"The point you are making escapes me," said Tennant.

"Yet it is surely clear. What error could be greater than that of taking these elderly gentlemen out of doors? What blunder more crass than that of describing to them natural beauties? Landor may have loved nature more than art, but I'm convinced that all of us, whatever we pretend, are much more fitted to discuss art than nature. We are urbane, and all our lives tend to make us more so. The Union is far more typical of Oxford than the Botanic Garden. If time presses, as our old friend Baedeker would put it, omit the Botanic Garden. Besides, men are more important than views and their ideas more important than the men themselves. My choice dictates itself—I shall take the Senators to Christ Church Hall in a closed vehicle and deliver my lecture on the portraits there. If the Senators show any appreciation of those portraits—as I think they will—I shall tell them of other artistic treasures in other Colleges, but that part of my discourse will be delivered seated in an armchair, and will perhaps require some sort of encouraging refreshment to give it flavour."

"As editor of the guide-book," said Tennant, "I entirely approve your choice."

"Very well then. We advance into that noble Hall, which I for one can never enter without a thrill, and the Senators observe for the first time the majestic grandeur of a sixteenth-century dining hall, and realise what a great dinner in such surroundings might mean."

"I wonder if Aristotle has dined in the replica of Christ Church Hall in Chicago?" asked Pacey.

"Ignoring that interruption, which is not in good taste, I draw their attention to the pictures. Here, I say, are four centuries of English portrait painting at its best. Look at the Reynolds of Archbishop Markham, look even more closely at these four portraits, two Gainsboroughs, a Romney, and a Reynolds, which hang together at the west end of the south wall, and see to what heights portrait painting could rise. Look again at the work of Shee and Pickersgill and Watts, and consider how nearly the great tradition of portrait painting maintained itself in the nineteenth century; look at the Orpen and the Orchardson, and regret that there is no Sargent beside them. Look, if you must, at the most recent portraits of all—though I shall avert my eyes. It is not, however, primarily to study art that you come here today. What you see before you is the great sweep of English history throughout four centuries, statesmen and soldiers, men of learning, judges, and divines. Nowhere else in England, save at the National Portrait Gallery, will the history of this country come before you with the same vivid continuity. Glance, for example, at the portrait of Bishop King by David Mytens, I think, and you see the calm certainty of a seventeenth-century religious man who has made his spiritual Odyssey and arrived at the haven where he would be—or examine the eager and questing beauty of the lean and intellectual face of John Wesley."

"Aren't you trying the Senators rather high?" enquired Tennant. "They may be expert in painting and may be learned in religious controversy, but I don't see Samson quite making the grade in either subject."

"Perhaps I am, but I shall have a story or two to attach to most of the portraits. Go back for a moment to the sixteenth-century examples—such as Henry VIII and Elizabeth. Not that the Henry VIII is either a Holbein or a sixteenth-century picture; it is more probably an eighteenth-century copy. Still, it does dominate the Hall as Henry would certainly have wished. When a team of

American professional golfers was visiting Oxford on their way through to Yorkshire, I happened to be in Christ Church, and it fell to me to show them the pictures. 'Ah,' said one of them—the captain, I think—'isn't that Henry VIII? He had a big influence on your Church history, didn't he?' I thought I could safely say 'Yes' to that. 'And what exactly was his influence on the Church of England?' asked another golfer. I confess that I shrank from a five minutes' exposé of Henry's ecclesiastical importance. I'd have given something to have had Mitton or Winn alongside just at that moment. 'Ah, well,' said one of the more tactful of the golfers who seemed to sympathise with my embarrassment, 'I suppose he was the big boy, anyhow'. And we compromised on that, though I have felt since that as a definition it was imperfect. And the Elizabeth—the last woman to dine on a formal occasion in the Hall until her present Majesty. There's a story connected with another royal visit, too, but it cannot perhaps with perfect propriety yet be told."

Waterlow smiled. "It will be a terribly long lecture, I'm afraid, for there's a story to every picture. Look at the two Lawrences side by side, and realise why Pitt thought so well of Eden and why few thought well of Canning. Look at Gladstone by Millais, and see the Oxford Gladstone. Can it be true, as I have heard it whispered, that he loved Oxford so much that he wished to be buried in his D.C.L. robes? Then, if Samson's attention is straying, I shall indicate to him the picture of William Penn, and point out the strange fact that he alone of all the company is depicted in armour. There's a subject for a sermon for you, Mitton, if ever you are asked to preach in the Cathedral. Or look at the haggard effigy of John Locke, a philosopher so eminent that he was dismissed from the House; or Busby, sometime headmaster of Westminster, a pedagogue true to his trade who thrashed so many schoolboys that he should be regarded as the true founder of the English public-school system. Or Dean Strong by Orpen, a picture more broad than high, and of this curious shape because, so they say, the classical dons of that day were incapable of distinguishing 'twixt length and breadth and unable to make their wishes known to the eminent artist. It is said, too, that the bishop —for so by that time Dean Strong was—had the greatest difficulty in holding Orpen to his engagements. When he had arranged a sitting the artist would cancel it and make a hasty dash to France —where he was engaged in painting that notorious murderer Landru. 'Bishops can wait, but the guillotine won't', was his excuse."

"I do not remember to have seen an Orpen of Landru," said Prendergast.

"But that, as you would yourself say, is no evidence that it was not painted. Most of all, I cherish some of the less well-known pictures. Speaker Abbot, who hangs on the north wall, has not left a great mark on history, yet it fell to him to give one of the great casting votes. Winn will remember, even if the rest of you have forgotten. It was on the motion that the case of Dundas should go to a committee—or, without technicalities, whether Dundas should be impeached or not. Pitt knew that Dundas, or Lord Melville as he then was, was his great, almost his only, prop, and he exerted all his influence to save his supporter. Influence meant something then, too, for there were many votes that went to the Prime Minister, however good or bad his cause might be. I think the crisis came when Wilberforce rose to speak, for of all men of that time his was the fairest record for integrity and high-mindedness, but he was the most loved, perhaps the only intimate, friend that Pitt had. So, as he rose to speak, Pitt, though he would ask a favour of no man, did (or so in imagination I see him) turn to him a questioning, almost an appealing, glance. Wilber-force spoke, and at first no man could tell in which direction his counsel lay, but at length only too clearly the verdict came and it was a verdict which turned against Melville. Even so, the event was doubtful, for the silent brute votes were not to be diverted from the ministerial side. The vote was taken and the numbers on either side were equal. Cornewall, the Speaker, turned ashy white and for two full minutes, so men say, he sat silent. I expect that Tennant would say this is only true in a guide-book sense. But he paused long enough to make the suspense almost unendurable, and then at last gave the casting vote which meant impeachment. Pitt pulled his hat over his eyes and hurried from the House, the tears trickling down his cheeks. 'We've killed the fox', shouted his opponents—in one sense an oddly inappropriate comment, in another curiously accurate, for it was the loss of Dundas much more than the loss of Austerlitz that was Pitt's death-stroke."

With the skill of the practised lecturer, Waterlow glanced at his audience to see whether he was holding their attention. Then he continued. "I always think that the really difficult question in a College Hall is to decide whether the eminence of the subject or the beauty of the picture shall be the deciding factor in securing hanging space. Pusey's is a posthumous portrait of little merit; Dodgson is depicted as a pale and unimpressive cleric, but how could either be excluded? Or look at Louis de Visme. He was ambassador to Sweden, or so at least the legend beneath tells us; but what real claim has he to hang among the mighty? One only. He was painted in a light-blue flowered waistcoat of entrancing beauty. How many generations of undergraduates must have been charmed by that graceful and lovely garment! If ever Oxford becomes a women's University, I prophesy that Louis de Visme's portrait will hang in the place of highest honour. But what a title to fame! The casual choice of a waistcoat on some sunny eighteenth-century morning!"

"I've wondered, too, about the choice of pictures in College Halls," said Gresham, "and I have sometimes felt a little cynical about the legends which are written beneath them. Read, for example, the list of honours and appointments beneath some of the portraits, and then go to Wadham and observe the most famous man of that College. 'Robert Blake, Admiral.' Just that and nothing more. There is fame."

"Good wine needs no bush," remarked Mitton, as indeed those who knew him best expected him to say.

"I think that Porson, or perhaps Aristotle, will ask you how Christ Church contrived to acquire so priceless a collection," suggested Tennant.

"I call that an intelligent question," said Waterlow, "because I am able to provide the answer. It was customary for distinguished persons to be painted in the eighteenth century; it was customary for them also to give their portraits to institutions or societies to which they had belonged. Sometimes, however, they were not alive to their responsibilities, and so you will see, if you search the Chapter minutes, that a formal letter would be written in which the Dean and Chapter would express a wish that the recipient of the letter would 'enable' them to place his portrait on the walls. That, I take it, was a courteous and flattering request for a gift. As time went on the formula changed a little, and as the phraseology became more stilted the flattery became more insidious. If my recollection is not at fault, something of this kind would be written: 'The Dean and Chapter have observed with satisfaction the honours which have come upon you; these have brought distinction both to yourself and to Christ Church, and the Dean and Chapter are therefore prepared to place your portrait in the Hall, if you will enable them to do so.' Very few men can be flattered too much. Still, the bait was not always swallowed. After Rosebery had become Prime Minister, the Dean and Chapter not unnaturally desired to see his portrait hanging on their walls; they wrote him a letter of the usual kind, and expected, no doubt, to acquire a fine and formal portrait by the leading artist of the day. They received instead a portrait of Rosebery as a very young man—no doubt, it was suggested by the donor, they would prefer to see him on their walls depicted as he had looked in undergraduate days. Would that not be a greater inspiration and incentive to the young? Perhaps it would have been if only they had not sent him down because he preferred attendance at the Derby to attendance at the prescribed lectures."

"I am beginning to think," said Tennant reflectively, "that for guide-book purposes pictures are a better starting-point than buildings or views—they certainly bring us more directly in touch with persons."

"If there is time," continued Waterlow, "I shall take the Senators to see another picture, and talk to them about earlier visitors as distinguished as themselves. It's an engraving of Blücher, and it hangs in the room which the Field-Marshal occupied when he came to Oxford with the Allied sovereigns in 1814. There's a story connected with that room and that picture too."

"You're not going to inflict the history of Blücher on us, I trust," said Prendergast in some alarm.

"Oh no, though I might tickle the Senators' fancy by telling them that he was cashiered from the Prussian Army near the beginning of his military career, or give them a useful piece of practical advice by telling them that he called all Russians by one of two names according to their rank, because two Russian names were all that he could remember. I'm concerned with his visit to Christ Church. He was sumptuously entertained, for he had the reputation of being a notable drinker. 'Is there anything else we can do for your comfort?' said the Canons of Christ Church as they conducted him (if that is the right word) to bed. 'Nothing,' replied the rugged soldier, 'except that you may lay a bottle of brandy beneath my pillow!' Next morning dawned and with it the scout to call the Field-Marshal to the labours of another day. But the Field-Marshal (or should I say the Prince, for he had received that title in June) was already striding round

Christ Church Meadow—and the brandy bottle was empty. That was the story and no one ever ventures to dispute its truth— yet I am sure that it is pure fable. Blücher, as you may learn from his letters, had a wholesome fear of the reputation of the English for heavy drinking; he announced on his arrival in this country that he would drink nothing but claret, and he proudly announced on his return to the Continent that he had kept his word and thus continued to hold his own with his hosts." (7)

Waterlow paused. "You know," he continued, "it appears to me that Blücher's famous remark when he saw Paris would be an admirable motto for our Oxford researches: '*Was für plündern!*' It's not quite so easy to translate as you might think. I fancy that 'What a place to have the plundering of!' gives the right shade of meaning. I always feel as I look round Oxford that every College and almost every house has its special treasures and that something of artistic merit is to be found behind almost every door. But perhaps I am straying too far from the portrait of Blücher, and I have talked too much. Robert, you haven't given us your own favourite view. What is it?"

Tennant hesitated a little before he replied.

"As I've listened to what the rest of you have said, I have come to the conclusion that I should never have used the word 'view' at all. It's the peculiar Oxford associations which matter, and not the actual prospect, however agreeable that may be. Please don't think that I've not enjoyed Winn on the High or Gresham on Worcester, for I certainly have—but for guide-book purposes I must admit that John Waterlow has provided the most material. For that reason I shall not choose anything very startling in itself, but rather something that will appeal to the Senators. I shall take them to the sweet shop in St. Aldate's."

"What is that?" asked Pacey. "I should have thought that sweet rationing had spoiled the view of most sweet shops."

"It's the authentic sweet shop which Alice visited in *Through*

"Alice's Shop", in St. Aldate's

the Looking-glass and where the sheep was knitting. You must know Tenniel's illustration—and your scientific mind will readily appreciate that in Looking-glass Country the shop is turned the other way round."

"A highly unscientific description, but I take your meaning."

"It seems to me that in that shop the Oxford of Lewis Carroll is still alive. Sweet ration or no sweet ration, I dare swear that the sweets in those glass bottles have not been changed since Tenniel drew them. I sometimes think that that odd world was the real Oxford. Is there any historical Oxford character better known than the White Knight or even the Walrus and the Carpenter?"

"That observation," commented Winn, "suggests an interesting speculation. Who is the best-known figure in English literature? Not Hamlet, not Mr. Pickwick, not even Robinson Crusoe, but without any shadow of doubt Sherlock Holmes. How many millions of people know him more intimately than their own relatives!"

"You might go further," suggested Tennant. "Are not some of the characters of fiction more real than historical personages? If it comes to historical evidence—evidence, I mean, which would convince Winn or any patient researcher—the character in the Middle Ages about whom we know most is surely the Devil. Think of it, he was seen and described by thousands of unimpeachable witnesses at hundreds of different times and in hundreds of different places. And by and large the descriptions tally. You can't get round all that evidence."

Gresham suddenly lapsed into one of his spasms of silent laughter. "I was calling to mind," he said, "when I stepped myself, so to speak, into Lewis Carroll's Oxford. A foolish little anecdote, but it might be worth incorporating in the guide-book. You know that it is possible to go underground and travel in a punt or a canoe right underneath the city. You go in just below the Castle and you come out about twenty minutes later in what used to be called Trill Mill Stream on the south side of Christ Church. It's only a large drain really, but the voyage is not unpleasant and it's exciting to hear the rumble of traffic above when you pass under Carfax. I fancy, though I don't know for certain, that this particular drain or waterway is used by Carroll when Alice makes her journey with the sheep. I made the journey myself one summer afternoon with three other men, and it so happened that when we emerged in what was then the new Christ Church Memorial Garden some people were leaning over the stone balustrade and looking at the stream as it flowed lazily out of the ground. Their faces when our canoe emerged stick in my memory—you see, it happened to be the day of Encænia and two of us were in morning coats and top-hats. I think that scene would have pleased Lewis Carroll; certainly we must have looked not unlike a Mad Hatter's water picnic. We might take the Senators down the drain if you think it could help them to recapture the authentic spirit of a bygone Oxford."

Tennant shook his head. "Tempted though I am to dig further in the rich vein of precious metal which Lewis Carroll provides," he said, "I really must exercise self-control, for there are two members of the team who have not yet had their innings. Pacey, what are you going to show the Senators?"

"That isn't very easy for me. You all know that I think that in the modern world it's the scientific work, the laboratories, and so forth, which represent the really important part of University life. But how can I take three elderly and probably ignorant gentlemen into my laboratory; they'd be bored to tears and they'd interrupt the work with futile questions. If one of them was a physicist or a chemist, it would be very different. He could spend a week in the Clarendon Laboratory or the Dyson Perrins and enjoy every minute of it—but as things are!" He made a gesture of frustration. "What earthly use is it to take a man who has no scientific background into a laboratory? Have you, Winn, or you, Gresham, ever been inside a laboratory in your lives? Have you ever been inside a great modern factory? I thought not, and yet you cheerfully go on repeating old-fashioned theories about a liberal education, and I believe you think that the world could be run according to the theories of half a dozen Greek philosophers who died I don't really know when."

"If you were a teacher of modern languages, as I am," Waterlow interrupted with a smile, "you would at this stage refer your audience to a modern French comedy of great merit, which bears the title *Knock, ou le triomphe de la médecine*. Dr. Knock had performed the rare feat of transforming a sleepy mountain hamlet where no one was ever ill into a fashionable *Kurort* where no one was ever well and where no single person (with an adequate income) was without his private ailment. Then when his predecessor visited him he described in a passage of singular power the scene which he conjured up at a certain hour of the day. (8) Can't you follow his example and draw a picture for the Senators which will show them the rows of zealous students bending like one man over their test-tubes and their specimens?"

Pacey grunted contemptuously.

"Seriously," said Tennant, "there is much in what Pacey has been saying. Many things are profoundly interesting to those who have some knowledge of them and useless for those who have not. Is it really profitable to take anyone except a bibliophile into a great library? I might show the Senators a Caxton or perhaps a first-folio Shakespeare, but where would we go from there? Probably they'd all three be much more interested in the conveying belt which passes books through Bodley than in any of the books themselves. I remember my father speaking to me of one of the great exhibitions of his boyhood. All the wonders of science and mechanical invention left the crowds uninterested—for everyone was fascinated by one single exhibit; that was a bunch of bananas. I suppose that it had only recently become possible to import bananas in bulk and that no one in England had seen a bunch of this strange fruit before."

"Are you not saying, in effect," objected Gresham, "only that your choice of objects to show them is at fault. If, then, none of them is a bibliophile—though I believe Porson will be—you should show them curiosities rather than precious books. Show them the ancient books chained to their shelves (that is as un-failing a success with the semi-educated as a visit to the polar bears at the Zoo), or show them fine and curious bindings, show them the signatures of famous men (and hear patiently their jocular and fatuous comments). We are hosts, Robert, and must suffer as hosts do. Or better still, show them in a College Library that rare, perhaps unique, page of a book which was once part of one of the most widely distributed works of the day."

Even Winn was at a loss to understand Gresham's last sug-gestion and craved enlightenment.

"It is a sheet out of the school book—the first and most ele-mentary school book, used all over England in the reign of Queen Elizabeth. Every child who learned to read must have read the book at that time; there must have been thousands, perhaps hundreds of thousands of copies, but—to cut the story short—no complete copy is known to have survived. Probably the book was too common for anyone to preserve it—at any rate, there it is, this single, unique sheet. There's a thought there for the student of social history, Winn!"

"So you don't escape, after all, Pacey," said Tennant, "though I did my best for you. Evidently the sense of the meeting is that you should show the Senators something. What is it to be, what sight, what curiosity, what view?"

Pacey looked a little shamefaced. "It so happens," he said, "that last week I was walking down South Parks Road with a post-graduate chap from New Zealand, over here to do a bit of medical research, and we reached the School of Pathology."

"You mean that modern building in the Parks, just by the turn to Parsons' Pleasure?" enquired Winn.

"Yes. Well, my friend stopped in front of the building and pointed to two windows on the first floor. Behind those windows he said, Florey and his team worked out the Penicillin business. I always stop here and look at those windows—for me it's the most beautiful view in the world."

Winn looked at Pacey with a new interest.

"Really, Pacey," he said with almost paternal approval, "I must congratulate you on your choice. There is always a close association between great men and the places in which they work. I wish Florey had been a St. Thomas's man! You must remind me to show you some day the room in our Old Buildings where, as I am almost though not quite certain, our first President completed his commentary on the odes of Horace."

"I'm not quite sure if it would affect me in just the same way as Florey's windows," murmured Pacey.

Tennant now turned to Trower. "Come on, Bursar, it's your turn. The last wicket but one has fallen, and Trower buckles on his pads, preparatory to playing a characteristic innings."

"And you think you can get the roller ready at the same time, don't you?" retorted the Bursar. "You may be deceiving yourselves, for I've seen a good many last-wicket stands that lasted a mighty long time. Don't underrate me, Tennant, if you want this guide-book to be a success. As that fellah Gilbert used to say, you know:

> *I am an intellectual chap*
> *And think of things that would astonish you.*

No one in Oxford ever gives a soldier credit for possessing any brains."

"Military criticism aside, what do you suggest as your contribution to this part of the guide-book?"

Trower helped himself to a large whisky and soda and settled himself again in his chair.

"First of all," he said, "I think this. You're mucking the whole business. There's a certain job in front of us, and instead of getting on with it we discuss theories and point out views to them. Bah! If a general comes down to inspect your brigade, you don't show him the view from the canteen window. The job of showing Oxford to three American visitors is a perfectly simple and straightforward one—you only want a programme and a time sheet, and remember to allow them plenty of time for lunch. It's as simple as falling off a log. But you must have your scheme and stick to it."

"That's all very well, Bursar, but you must show them something, and we agreed to leave St. Thomas's to Winn at the end. What are you going to choose to show them? Let your æsthetic sense have full play."

"Æsthetic sense be damned," replied Trower, who was always ready to change his line of argument. "You're all wrong about that too. The view doesn't matter, it's what you connect with it. If I go for a walk in the country, I'm thinking how a high pheasant would come out of that wood on the side of the hill, or whether there's a fish in the stream at the bottom. I suppose if I'd ever been a hunting man I'd think differently. What's the good of showing Keble to those Senator wallahs and telling them it's like the Rock of Gibraltar as someone suggested last night? They don't know what Keble means, and I don't suppose they've even seen Gib. If you'd been stationed there, as I was, for more than two years, you'd think it a bloody awful view. Sorry, Mitton, you don't like swearing, but honestly some of the theories I've listened to make me ill."

"I've every sympathy with much of what you say," said Tennant, whose long experience of Trower had taught him that the Bursar usually had a sensible suggestion to make if he were

THE RIVER IN EIGHTS WEEK, from the painting by Evelyn Dunbar

allowed to let off steam first, "but I can't help pointing out that your criticisms are more destructive than constructive. Come on, old warrior, you must play ball with us and tell us the best way to exhibit Oxford to the Senators."

"Well," said Trower somewhat mollified, "I see it like this. I haven't got much sympathy for the one you call Aristotle, and Porson seems to wallow in intellectual nonsense, but I have a sort of fellow feeling for this chap Samson, and I don't think for a minute that the curve of the High or Worcester Gardens or even a portrait of Gladstone would mean a thing to him. If I took him to London I might show him the Trooping the Colour and I'd certainly take him to Lord's in the summer or to Twickenham or Wembley in the winter, but I shouldn't waste time over the Tower or the British Museum. What I'm driving at is this. If you want to show these Senators Oxford properly, you've got to show them men doing things. Take them to the river, or the running track, or to the Parks. I'll bet you Samson will imagine one of his own boys rowing down the course or getting what he'll call a home run in the Parks. It's not the views or the inanimate objects that count, but human nature and human beings."

" 'Out of the mouths of babes and sucklings'," quoted Mitton, not very appositely.

Trower bristled. "I'm not a babe and suckling, and I'll trouble you to remember it," he growled.

Mitton was overcome with confusion. "I'm really very sorry," he said. "I must learn to bridle the unruly member."

"If that means keeping your trap shut, I second the motion," was Trower's not very delicate reply.

"You've got to be a little careful if you take Americans to a cricket match," interposed Prendergast. "I did it once, and I shall not easily forget the experience. It was in the twenties, I think, and there were some American professors over here from Yale. It was the time when Yale was going over to the residential system, and they wanted to study conditions of College life over here. For some reason or other the Vice-Chancellor handed them over to me for an afternoon so that they could see something of Oxford games, and I unwisely started by showing them a game of cricket in the Parks. It was a lovely warm afternoon and I spent the time as we walked up in explaining the game to them—a difficult task, much more difficult than describing the constitution of the University. As you all know, I am not a very good cricketer, but I am a very good lawyer, and also, if I may say so, a superlatively good draughtsman and expositor."

"The precise meaning of a phrase much used by my pupils," said Gresham, "is now apparent to me. It sounds like 'Sez you'."

"I am only giving an unprejudiced account of my own qualifications, and I repeat that it would be difficult to name any-one better qualified to explain the rather intricate rules of the game of cricket to persons unacquainted with its rudiments. My method was simple: I described with great care all the various ways in which it was possible to get out, for that was a part of the game on which I felt myself to be experienced. Bowled and stumped and caught and all the rest of it. My three professors expressed themselves as much interested and, by the time we reached the Parks, fully competent to appreciate the finer points of the game. When, however, we sat down in front of the pavilion I realised that I had made a great error. Gloucestershire were batting and my heart sank when I observed that Dipper was what the Americans called 'at strike'. Now Dipper's characteristic as a batsman, as some of you will remember, was that he never got out. (I at least never remember to have seen him dismissed, though I suppose he must have got tired eventually and got himself out when most of us had left). My confidence was not increased when I saw that it was Sinfield—no, it wasn't, it was surely Hammond at the other end—Hammond clearly in the mood to take a little quiet practice at the expense of the rather erratic University bowling. We settled into our seats and the professors began to make bets with each other which of my 'ways of getting out' they would see first. I remember that one of them was very confident that 'playing the ball twice' or the 'two-minutes rule' would be the winner—I think he must have been a brother lawyer. I simply hadn't the heart to tell them if a wicket fell at all that day we could think ourselves lucky. Then there was a very awkward moment. Hammond, or perhaps Dipper, hit an enormous balloon and was well caught in the deep. Unfortunately the umpire had called a no-ball; that involved me in a lot of explanation, and I don't think I really persuaded them that someone had not been cheating. Luckily the sun was shining and the air was balmy, and so to my relief two of my guests dropped off to sleep—perhaps they dreamed of Babe Ruth. One, however, a professor of Spanish, never took his eyes off the game. For over after over he watched—at the end of every over he gave a little sigh of disappointment, but he never wavered in his belief that sooner or later the great moment would come. Even when Cambridge have been batting at Lord's I've never wanted a wicket to fall as much as I did then. And then at last, unbelievably, the great moment came. Hammond, or was it Sinfield, after all, I can't remember—Hammond, let us say, touched a ball and was caught at the wicket. My Spanish professor could hardly contain himself; he turned to his two companions and dug them in the ribs. 'Wake up, wake up,' he cried, 'it's true, after all!' With confidence restored, I ventured to ask a question. 'Well,' said I, 'we talked a lot about cricket and I've explained everything to you. Is there any little point you haven't quite understood? If there is, I'll be glad to make it clear.' The first two professors had had more than enough and they shook their heads vigorously and said it was all as plain as plain could be, but the Spanish professor was tougher. He thanked me very gracefully for the clarity of my exposition, but said that he was not quite certain about one small point. Would I be so kind as to tell him the exact difference between two words which I had frequently used—the pitch and the wicket."

Gresham laughed. "And how did the superlatively good expositor deal with that question?"

"I cannot deny that he gave the American best. In point of fact, I looked at my watch, exclaimed that I had not noticed before how late it was, and urged them to hasten to the river if they wished to see the eights at practice."

"Perhaps the guide-book should keep clear of cricket," said Tennant. "Besides, we are handicapped by the fact that it's vacation and I don't see how we can show the Senators the under-graduates at play. What can you do about that, Bursar? Doesn't it knock out your proposal?"

Trower shook his head obstinately. "We can, at any rate, show them where 'Varsity sport does take place and explain how the eights are organised and all that sort of thing. And if you're all so damned keen on argument, we can discuss whether sport plays too big a part in undergraduate life—though for my part I'd much rather send half the scholars down and fill up with men who know how to live a decent open-air life. A lot of you seem to forget that the University has to turn out administrators and government servants and empire builders, as well as academic persons like yourselves."

Tennant hastened to pour oil on waters which looked as if they would be troubled. "It's rather late to plunge into that argument," he said, "though I agree that the guide-book ought not to shirk such a well-known and contentious issue. Perhaps we should postpone it till we talk about College life."

"All right by me," said Trower. "Now, Mitton, you can per-form the operation which you would call pouring coals of fire on my grey head and I should call another large whisky and soda."

CHAPTER V

"THE more I think about it," began Tennant, "the more do I feel convinced that the Bursar hit the nail on the head when he said last night that we ought to concentrate on the daily life of men here."

"I thought the same," Gresham agreed, "and I was reminded of an incident that happened last winter. An old member of the College, a former American Rhodes Scholar, came over and called on me, for our President happened to be away. He had had a distinguished career and had become the head—President I suppose he would be called—of an American University. I think he had not been back to Oxford since he went down twenty-five years or so ago. It was a pleasure rather than a duty to show them the College, for both he and his wife were charming, modest, and friendly persons. The only fly in the ointment was that we were followed round by a photographer who was apparently under contract to provide suitable pictures for America of the President's visit to his old College. All three of us were embarrassed, but there was nothing that we could do except try to get the operation finished as soon as might be. 'Now, Mr. President; I want you in a characteristic pose as you were in your undergraduate days', said the photographer. The badgered guest replied that he had no characteristic pose, but his wife made the suggestion that he should be photographed in his old rooms, and accordingly to his old rooms we went. Fortunately the rooms were inhabited by a studious undergraduate who had a respectable number of books on his shelves. 'And now,' said the photographer, 'take up your characteristic pose in your old rooms. Where did you sit and study ?' A happy smile came over the President's face. 'Now it all

137

comes back to me,' he said. 'I'm sure I spent half my time at Oxford poking my fire. You borrow me a poker and I'll show you a characteristic pose—the English open fire has a great reputation in the States—though not for warmth.' We borrowed a poker and a scuttleful of coal (though we didn't light it) and put him in a low armchair, gripping his poker in his right hand, and then to satisfy the proprieties I selected a book and made him hold it in his left."

"What did you give him?" asked Tennant.

"Mill on Liberty; I thought that suitable. It made a happy and homely picture and I hope created all the right impressions when it reached America."

"Excellent," said Tennant, "your story entirely confirms my view. Let us describe the daily life of an Oxford undergraduate to the Senators. I feel pretty sure that they'll find as much interest in an ordinary set of undergraduate's rooms as in, say, the Divinity Schools or the Sheldonian. Isn't it true that social history is much more interesting to most people than political or constitutional history?"

"It's not so easy to describe a day in someone else's life," put in Prendergast. "I suggest that it would be better to describe a typical day in our own undergraduate time; we shall soon see how things have changed and what the differences are. Come on, Winn, you are the oldest; describe a day in your life when you first came up."

"Really," said Winn, "I'm not quite sure if I can do that. My memory is dreadfully defective, you know, and I forget the simplest things nowadays."

"You mustn't be coy," said Prendergast. "Come on, I'll give you a start, and you'll find that it will go as easily as possible. Something like this, I think: Chapter I. It was a beautiful winter morning in the late eighties when our hero Winn, jumping lightly from his bed, tumbled into his hot bath, shaved himself rapidly with his trusty cut-throat, and then sat down to one of the Gargantuan breakfasts which were fashionable in those days. There you are, I've given you the local colour and a good start, and you can go on with your day from there."

"No, no," protested Winn, "that's historically quite incorrect. I assure you it wasn't like that in any way. It was not in the eighties at all. I didn't come up till the beginning of the nineties, and there were no baths at St. Thomas's or, indeed, at any other College in my day. Let me see, we used to go with a can in the afternoons to a tap by the kitchen and get boiling water from there. In some Colleges they had big stone or earthenware jars which used to stand by the fire and get boiling hot—but we went to the tap. Yes—and then I used to pour the water into a tin hip-bath in front of my sitting-room fire. Dear me, how it all comes back to me. I used to have my tea on the floor beside me. Very sybaritic, Prendergast, but highly agreeable. Muffins and crumpets and chocolate cake by the side of the hip-bath—dear me, that was really luxury! But of course that was in the afternoon after rowing or games; in the morning we had a cold tub. No gentleman would think of missing his cold bath in the morning, winter or summer. I can't tell you how a man's reputation would have suffered if he had not taken a regular cold bath."

Winn shook his head in retrospective disapproval. Then a new idea struck him. "And your ridiculous remark about breakfast, Prendergast! Of course we went to chapel as soon as we had had our tub and dressed."

"Was chapel compulsory?" asked Pacey.

"Certainly it was—in every College. I think we had to go five times a week, it never occurred to us to think that strange or un-reasonable. And the Dean fined us half a crown if we missed a chapel—I remember that very well, though I think I never had to pay myself. At some Colleges they had a different system— they had to keep thirty-six or forty chapels in a term." Winn gave a gentle chuckle. "Why, I remember a friend of mine, a rather disreputable friend, you know, who told me that he was dormy thirty-eight down one term. I didn't know what he meant, for golf was only just coming in."

"But do you think that any reasonable society could justify compulsory chapel?" said Pacey.

"Indeed I do. It was just part of our College life, and how could daily attendance at chapel harm anyone?"

"I'm not religious, but even if I were I should decline absolutely to go to any service in which there was any element of compulsion," retorted Pacey obstinately.

"What has the Chaplain to say to that?" enquired Tennant. Mitton looked a little harassed. "I cannot," he said, "do other than agree with Winn when he speaks of the importance of daily worship in a community such as ours. None the less, I have always been a strong believer in the liberty of the individual conscience, and I should be very loth to compel any man to come to a service if he did not wish to do so. On the whole, I think that I must say that I am against compulsion."

"Then you're wrong," said Trower with his usual bluntness. "There has been no greater mistake made in Oxford than the abolition of compulsory chapel, except of course the admission of women and the abolition of compulsory Greek. Changes are nearly always a mistake. A little discipline is good for every young man, and there are few enough rules, anyway. Besides, every concession of that kind to modern ideas of liberty only makes men more critical of every sound rule or custom that's left. I tell you that the men only come along and badger me—crabbing the grub and that sort of thing—because they haven't anything else to grumble about. If Mitton would make them go to chapel, they'd be as happy as sandboys protesting that their consciences were outraged, and I should be left in peace. I say have rules and make the men keep them."

Tennant laughed. "I seem to hear Bacon's counsel to James I—
'give the Parliament good Commonwealth bills to discuss, that
an empty stomach do not feed upon humour'. That's sound
advice, but somehow I don't think the guide-book can very well
advocate compulsory chapel only on the ground that it will stop
complaints of the food in Hall. What do you say, Gresham?"

"I don't think that it's a simple question at all. On the one hand,
I have often thought that chapel is one of the places, as Hall is,
where the whole College ought to meet together. That adds, I
feel, to an appreciation of our corporate life. And then again I've
often been impressed by the value for many men of a quiet
quarter of an hour when they can think things over or even listen
subconsciously to those beautiful prayers. I'm talking of men who
are not 'religious' in the ecclesiastical sense. Yes, I'm certain that
we tend to underrate the personal benefit which comes to each
individual from a regular attendance at a service in College
Chapel. But there's the other side to be considered. I can appreciate that in our undergraduate days when everyone came up
straight from school, it was reasonable to treat them as though
they were still young enough to need discipline, but I can't feel
that conditions are the same now, when we live in an age of wars
and national emergencies." His voice became serious. "If I may
do so without offence, let me put it like this. You cannot say to
the men at one moment: 'You are really only a schoolboy and
are much too young to decide for yourself in such matters';
and at the next moment: 'You are a man now, fully competent
to serve your country and if necessary to die in your country's
service'. I can't make it rhyme like that. It's the same argument
which justified the lowering of the age to vote, isn't it? No, really
I cannot support compulsory chapel for men who in all other
matters are thought to be capable of making their own choice.
Regretfully, very regretfully, I must say that I should be opposed
to any return to the old rules. Build up a tradition if you can that

attendance at chapel is expected of men, unless they have conscientious objection, but don't introduce compulsion."

Tennant nodded. "Yes," he said, "I do not think that the guide-book can go the whole way, as Trower would wish, but it can perhaps mention the contradictory views which are held. We might use our old technique of putting it up to the Senators and hearing what they think."

"Isn't it time," asked Prendergast, "for us to hear more of that day in Winn's life? We left him, you know, stranded in his compulsory chapel and without his breakfast. What did you do, Winn, for the rest of the day?"

Winn looked a little pathetic, as he turned to Tennant.

"My dear Tennant," he said, "I do beg you to believe that I am anxious to do my utmost to assist in the compilation of your guide-book, but my memory is terribly hazy. It is the oddest thing, you know, but I find it almost impossible to remember in detail how I passed the time when I was an undergraduate."

"I expect you did a good deal of work, didn't you?" enquired Prendergast.

"Oh yes, indeed. I worked very hard. Now you remind me, I think that I must have read a good deal in the mornings, though I have a distinct impression that the most valuable work was done late at night, especially when I went into digs and found things quieter. In the mornings I went to an occasional lecture, but I did not gain very much from that. Didn't Dr. Johnson say that you could teach chemistry or boot-mending from lectures, but little else? Still, lectures were part of the Oxford system; lectures and the reading of essays to tutors and examinations—I suppose those were the three characteristic things in our working life."

"The odious word 'tutorial' seems to be almost universally used nowadays," lamented Gresham.

"You are fortunate," retorted Prendergast, "if no one has yet referred to it in your hearing as a 'tute'."

"Dear me," said Winn, "I had no idea that the deterioration of undergraduate speech had gone so far. But shall I tell you more about the work we did when I came to St. Thomas's?"

"I think we'll postpone that topic till later," replied Tennant rather hastily. "I have a presentiment that the Senators will ask us whether men work much harder nowadays than in the past, and I think that we ought to treat the question as a separate topic. Tell us, rather, how you passed the rest of the day."

Winn polished his glasses and considered what answer he should give.

"I am sure, now that I think of it, that we had a very light luncheon, or rather a very plain luncheon. My recollection is that most men used to have a commons of bread and cheese, a pint of beer, and a lot of marmalade. Dear me, we must have had very good stomachs! Of course directly after lunch we hurried off to the river; everyone at St. Thomas's was expected to row unless he was quite exceptionally good at games. Rowing, you see, was the great College sport—when the races were on the whole College used to run with the boat."

"What did you do in the evenings?" asked Prendergast.

Winn thought again. "Really I can't get a clear picture," he admitted at length. "I can remember that we used to collect in someone's rooms and sing songs and play cards and so on, and I can remember going to the theatre and to the Union, and, much better, going to one or other of our literary clubs. That's the clearest recollection of all—we used to read papers and discuss things and talk and talk and talk. But I cannot have spent all my evenings at clubs of that kind. I think I must have worked on many evenings, but I just cannot remember. No, the more I think about those things the more sure I am that it was the talking and discussion that was the best part of our lives. Please do forgive me for giving you such a dreadfully dull account of what we did in my day—I never realised how much I had forgotten it all."

"Not at all," said Tennant, "I think you've given us a good start. I can picture your life quite well, and it's in accordance with custom that you should have forgotten all the working hours. I remember a Professor of Divinity who was also a Canon of Christ Church. He told me that he had been brought up on the principle that no gentleman works after dinner. When he had been a Canon for a year or two he told me that he had adopted a second principle—that no gentleman ever works after lunch. But I'm sure that he was a worker, and he has, indeed, received well-merited preferment. Isn't it true that almost everyone disguises the amount of work that he does? Didn't that prolific poet Byron look on his writing as something done in his spare time when he was not occupied in being a gentleman? But I suppose he wrote more lines in a few years than any other poet."

"I don't know about that," said Prendergast, "but I am sure that the first great shock which comes to the young when they go down is to find that they have to work after lunch. The afternoon has for so long been sacred to enjoyment. Then comes the acid test of character—the office stool in the afternoon. But we mustn't let ourselves get distracted from our main object. We asked Winn to describe a day in his young life in order that we might the better describe the life of the modern undergraduate to the Senators. Do you think that there have been many changes? I don't. Every day one hears complaints that Oxford is only a pale shadow of its former self, but it seems to me that the similarities are much more marked than the differences. They have communal meals, and the old private hospitality has to a large extent gone, but what other changes—essential changes—are there? Don't men still discuss everything in heaven and earth as they always did? And didn't I hear Winn say that that was the thing that mattered most? What's your view, Gresham?"

A shy, deprecating smile lighted up Gresham's sensitive face. He had both greater possibilities for enjoyment and perhaps for suffering than the others. When he spoke his hesitation was in marked contrast to Prendergast's clipped and legal tones.

"The curious fact, and the fact that I cannot explain but can only be thankful for," he said, "is that, try as I will, I only remember the happy days. And, furthermore, I only remember the ordinary days. The big occasions have all faded from my mind. I don't mean to say that the sun was always shining. You must all in your turn have experienced those strangely fascinating evenings in late October or early November when the night seems to be falling before the afternoon is over, when there's a mist or fog turning the streets into dim and romantic alleys and when you hurry to Blackwell's to buy a book before closing time comes. Or I think of my own rooms as a freshman—perhaps that's the most important thing of all. For the first time I seemed to have an individuality of my own, where I could dream my dreams and live my own individual existence. The author who chose that title *A Room of One's Own* had the root of the matter in her. And the summer days too—in summer-time the sun did always shine then. I can see myself sitting on the bank in the Quad having lunch—yes, Winn is quite right, it used to be bread and cheese and beer on most days. We used to put the tortoises in the middle of the grass in the quadrangle and make bets which of them would find its way back to the shade of the flower-beds first. But this is unpardonable of me, I'm meandering on, and not helping at all. I really must try to be more explicit. You asked whether I thought conditions had changed much, Prendergast, did you not?"

"Yes, that was the question."

"I believe that I could answer it now," interjected Winn, who had followed Gresham's remarks with close attention. "It seems to me that we had more pleasure than the modern undergraduate because to a large extent we provided it for ourselves. I know that I am old-fashioned but I do deplore the mechanisation of the present age, yes and the professionalisation of everything too. In

my day everything was, so to speak, on an amateur basis. There
were no cinemas and no wireless then; if we wanted a jovial
evening we got someone to play the piano and we all sang—not
very well, I fancy, but we enjoyed it. Nowadays an undergraduate seems to feel aggrieved if there are not more than two
good pictures to choose from every evening. Of course we went
to the theatre sometimes, but there was only one theatre and we
visited it only seldom."

"Wasn't there a music-hall of some sort?" asked Tennant.

"Oh yes, of course there was. The old East Oxford Theatre on
the Cowley Road, but men only went there on Saturday nights,
and I'm afraid that they only went to rag the show—very
reprehensible, but it became a sort of tradition. I doubt if the
Saturday performance often finished without disorder." Winn
chuckled. "How one thing brings back another! I remember that
one year when St. Thomas's had its turn for proctor, we elected
our philosophy tutor. One Saturday night he saw an undergraduate hurrying eastward over Magdalen Bridge and clasping
a large parcel to his body under his greatcoat. The proctor, so he
told me, asked the young man to unfold his parcel and show him
what he was carrying. He did so, unwillingly, and disclosed a
large fish—a turbot or hake or some such thing. The proctor felt
very sure that the hake would shortly be projected on to the stage
of the East Oxford Theatre, but of course he could not assume
that. 'Why,' he said, in his sternest tone of voice, 'why are you
carrying this fish?' 'Oh, Sir,' replied the undergraduate, 'I thought
it was a sound thing to have about me.' Now that was a very good
answer, especially to a proctor who was also a philosopher. It
would be difficult for a philosopher to decide, without adequate
argumentation, that a large hake was not a sound thing to have
about you at ten p.m. on a Saturday evening. Besides, the
marshall and the bulldogs were making it clear by their demeanour that they were most unwilling to carry this immense fish

back with them. The proctor took the prudent and sensible course; he ordered the undergraduate back to his College, and fined him next day for being out after dark without cap and gown." (9)

"I think Winn is right," said Gresham, "in saying that the amusements of those days were less professional than those of to-day—but I have another difficulty, and a more practical one. To put it very shortly, I'm not quite sure that we can describe the daily life of the undergraduate to the Senators, because I doubt if we ourselves properly appreciate the thoughts and feelings of the young. Does any one generation ever enter fully into the thoughts and ideas of the next?"

"Oh, come," said Tennant, "we live all the year round among the undergraduates—we teach them, we talk to them, and we talk about them. Surely if any men understand the young it is ourselves."

It was again Winn who broke into the conversation with another story. "I know, or perhaps I should say that I believe I know, the meaning of Gresham's criticism," he said, "and I am in agreement, or perhaps I should say partial agreement, with it. Many of us as we get older only dimly realise the changes which are taking place before our eyes. I remember once when poor Hargreaves, who was Dean then, was absent owing to some trifling illness—let me see, what was it? Influenza? No, I don't think so; wasn't it some complaint that men usually have much earlier in life, indeed in childhood, or was it that he had some accident? Dear me, my memory grows worse and worse. What *was* that illness?"

"Perhaps you will remember later on," said Tennant gently. "Tell us the story, anyhow."

"Ah yes, the story. I was acting as Dean, since Hargreaves, as I told you, was absent owing to this wretched illness—I wish I could remember what it was—and most unfortunately a

St. Thomas's undergraduate got into serious trouble. He was a scholar, a quiet, inoffensive man, who worked with the greatest assiduity and who we confidently expected would secure a first class in Moderations, even if he was not quite up to the standard of a first in Greats. He rowed, I recollect, in the third torpid, and his boat did quite well in the races. I recollect thinking that this success would give him confidence and be of advantage to him. You may judge, then, of my horror and surprise when I learned that he had become terribly intoxicated in the evening, and that, after breaking lamps and windows in College, he had climbed out of College and committed all sorts of atrocities in the streets—I think he smashed a plate-glass window, and assaulted a policeman and threw bottles at Oxford citizens—a terrible performance."

"It's always the quiet man who is most destructive when he runs amok," commented Tennant. "The real reprobate always gets away with it, for he knows how far he can go. I expect your friend was a teetotaler by nature, wasn't he?"

"Yes, and a scholar too. Worst of all, I was informed in the morning that he had been sent down by the Vice-Chancellor and proctors. Dear me, I remember how agitated and unhappy I was."

"What did you do?" asked Prendergast.

"I knew that I ought to have gone to the proctors, for it was their business, but I knew the Vice-Chancellor well, and so I turned to him. I asked for an appointment, and the Vice-Chancellor very courteously agreed to see me that afternoon. When I arrived I told him my story without circumlocution. 'The man in question has,' I said, 'been sent down by the proctors; no doubt his behaviour fully deserves this punishment, but he is a scholar of St. Thomas's and his conduct up to this unhappy moment has been blameless. If he is sent down a promising career will be irremediably ruined; I beg you, Mr. Vice-Chancellor, to intervene and save him from such a disaster.' The Vice-Chancellor was most sympathetic. 'Nothing, my dear Winn,' he said, 'would give me more pain than to damage the career of this worthy young man. I will speak to the proctors and ask them to revise their sentence of rustication. What shall we do with him? Ought he to be gated for a month instead?' 'No,' I said, 'he never goes out of College, and so gating would be meaningless—perhaps a fine would be more appropriate.' 'Certainly,' said the Vice-Chancellor, 'he must be fined £50 and we'll say no more about it. That will stop him from giving a wine for the next week or two.' At that moment I felt like Lot pleading with the Almighty. 'Mr. Vice-Chancellor,' I said, 'you have been so kind and sympathetic that I will venture to ask you another favour. This man is a poor scholar; he does not know what a wine means. He entertains his friends, I suspect, to an occasional cup of cocoa. Fifty pounds is a sum of money outside his comprehension—he has never heard of such a sum—and a fine of this amount would, I fear, mean the end of his career.' 'Dear me,' replied the Vice-Chancellor, 'I had no idea that undergraduates of St. Thomas's lived in such straitened circumstances! What do you think I should do?' 'Well,' said I, 'I think that a fine of a sovereign would cause him some inconvenience, and I feel sure that he will not offend again.' 'Certainly, my dear Winn. I'll suggest to the proctors that they fine him a sovereign. I am really much obliged to you for preventing what might have been a miscarriage of justice.' So you see it all ended happily, but I couldn't help thinking afterwards that the Vice-Chancellor was still living in a Victorian Oxford."

"And what did the proctors have to say?" enquired Prendergast dryly.

"Oh, I've just remembered," said Winn, "it was *chicken-pox*, that was the disease—chicken-pox. How could I have forgotten that! Poor Hargreaves, it was humiliating for him."

Waterlow laughed. "It may have been humiliating, but I think it must have saved that undergraduate some money. You and Gresham may be right, Winn, in thinking that one generation does not understand the next, but isn't it sometimes rather a matter of form and observance of conventions than of actual failure to understand? Let me tell you a little tale too, to illustrate what I mean. I had an undergraduate friend at one of the smaller colleges, an exhibitioner in natural science and a very eminent athlete. He played Rugger several times for England whilst he was still up. I met him one afternoon in the Club, and found him in an agitated state. I asked him what might the matter be. He replied that he had been selected to play for England against Ireland in Dublin—a match which meant three nights away— and that the President of his College had refused him leave to go. I pricked up my ears at this, for I knew the President—a man full of idiosyncrasies but, to my knowledge, of kind heart and ready sympathy. 'Tell me,' I said, 'what passed at the interview.' 'Oh,' said Stortford—for so I shall call him though it was not his name— 'I went round, as I always do, to the President's house, and I said "Please, Mr. President, may I have leave off for three nights next week—I've been asked to play Rugger for England at Dublin?" "What is your place in the field, Mr. Stortford?" "I play in the scrum—as a matter of fact, I'm a wing forward." "No, Mr. Stortford, I am not able to give you my permission to absent yourself—good morning." What do I do now? I simply must play—it never crossed my mind that the President would have the faintest objection to my going—he's always been interested in my football!' Now I knew that the President was a stickler for form and for the proprieties of language, so I told Stortford to return to his College, to ask if he might have an appointment with the President, and then to make his request in due form as though he had never asked before. The second interview passed, so I was informed, somewhat after this manner. 'Mr. President,'

said the undergraduate, 'I have requested permission to call on
you in order that I may ask your leave to absent myself from the
College for three nights during the coming week.' 'And for
what purpose, Mr. Stortford?' 'I have received an invitation from
the English Rugby Football Union to represent the Union in a
football match against Ireland next Saturday, Sir.' 'Can you
keep your term if you make this journey?' 'I have consulted the
Dean and Bursar, Sir, and have ascertained that I can pernoctate
without difficulty for the requisite number of nights in full
term.' 'And what is your position in the field, Mr. Stortford?'
'I play in the scrimmage, Mr. President.' 'Ah, it is a great honour
to be a member of the English scrimmage. I hope that there is
plenty of good hacking. You have my permission to be absent
for three nights.'"

Everyone laughed, though Winn looked a little mystified.

"My point is," said Waterlow, "that the older generation
sometimes understands rather more of the younger than is
immediately obvious. I should not be surprised, Winn, if your
Vice-Chancellor had a clearer picture of the life of your peccant
scholar than he let you know, and perhaps even [he added in a
lower voice which Winn could not hear] he had a better understanding of you than he allowed you to suspect."

Trower was growing a little impatient, and now burst into
the conversation. "At the risk of being repetitive," he said, "I
must insist that we are wasting our time. If we really want to
tell these Senators what the lives of undergraduates are like, why
don't we get on with the job? You're a practical chap, Prendergast, what do you remember of your undergraduate days?"

"My recollections seem to be precisely the opposite of Gresham's. He remembers the ordinary days, I remember the extra-
ordinary ones—above all, the riots and rags and such-like. I
suppose that's because I'm a lawyer; it is the occasion when the
law is broken that excites my interest."

"Now that's interesting," said Tennant. "Hume, you know, says that the philosopher infers God from the orderly arrangement of things, but that the pagan savage infers him from the apparent interruptions of order—the tempests and the eclipses and the earthquakes. Gresham seems to be Christian and you, David, are pagan. But tell us, for the benefit of the guide-book, about some of these noisy days and noisier nights that remain in your memory. That ought to make a good chapter for the guide-book, and no doubt the rest of us can fill in a few extra details. I suggest that Prendergast now gives his lecture on University breaches of discipline and decorum."

Prendergast laughed. "Well, I'll try. I don't think I need go back to the earlier riots—for they always took the same form—battles between town and gown, and bloody battles at that. If Porson or Aristotle turns out to be historically minded, Winn, no doubt, will tell them the tale of St. Scholastica's Day in 1354; that I suppose was the first great engagement. A later battle between town and gown would, I think, be more interesting—let me see if I can find it." He selected a book from amongst those Oxford books which Tennant had placed in the Common Room, and found the passage he sought.

"Yes, here it is—it comes from *Our Memories*. Denison, who is the writer, and who was a pro-proctor at the time of the 1832 'Reform' riots, had been struck by a large stone and carried unconscious to Oriel. 'My dear old friend the then Master of Balliol, Dr. *Jenkyns*, was just sitting down to dinner. He said—"What is all this disturbance outside?"—"Master, it is a great fight—Town and Gown; they say that Mr. *Denison* of Oriel is killed." He said—"Give me my Academicals, and open the door of the house into the street". The household represented the danger of doing this. The answer was—"Give me my Academicals and open the door". The Master stood on the doorsteps, and had just said to Town—"*My deluded friends*"—when a

TOWN AND GOWN, from the original sketch by the author of *Verdant Green*

heavy stone was pitched into the middle of his body, and he fell back into the arms of his servants, crying out "close the door". Upon this it was replied that many of the young gentlemen were outside to support him. He repeated "close the door": and was borne in, someone inside taking possession of the stone, which he preserved carefully!'

"That's first class! All my life I've been wanting to hear a Dean or Proctor address an unruly crowd as 'my deluded friends'. How intimate, how happy, how confidential! Seriously, the persistence of the tradition of these town and gown struggles, especially on November 5, is remarkable. It is a central theme in all the Victorian books on Oxford, and don't forget that these books have drawn a picture which later writers can never hope to obliterate or even to amend. Half the world still thinks that *Verdant Green* (10) and *Tom Brown at Oxford* represent the truth, the whole truth, and nothing but the truth (though some might add *Zuleika Dobson*). The town-and-gown battle always took the same course—the outnumbered but more skilful representatives of the gown invariably defeated the gigantic but clumsy townsfolk. I confess that my sympathies as I read were always on the side of the defeated; they never had a chance, for the writers were against them. Sometimes I have wondered if town-and-gown rows were not artificially provoked by the professors of what the books call 'the manly art' in order to encourage undergraduates to take lessons in boxing. But I must not pause too long over this part of my subject, for it belongs to a bygone age. I'm concerned rather with the ordinary high-spirited breaches of discipline and the hoaxes to which those in authority are liable. The *locus classicus* for that is in a book which will not, I think, be in Robert's library. Yes, by Jove, it is—let me read you this passage from *Vice Versa*. Mr. Tinkler, you'll remember, was the usher—I always regret that he was at Cambridge instead of at Oxford.

" ' "Talking of smoking," he went on, with a soft chuckle, as at recollections of unspeakable devilry, "did I ever tell you chaps of a tremendous scrape I very nearly got into up at the 'Varsity? Well, you must know there's a foolish rule there against smoking in the streets. Not that that made any difference to some of us! Well, one night about nine, I was strolling down Petty Cury with two other men, smoking (Bosher of 'Pothouse' and Peebles of 'Cats', both pretty well known up there for general rowdiness, you know—dear old friends of mine!) and, just as we turned the corner, who should we see coming straight down on us but a Proctor with his bull-dogs (not dogs, you know, but the strongest 'gyps' in College). Bosher said, 'Let's cut it!' and he and Peebles bolted. (They were neither of them funks, of course, but they lost their heads.) I went calmly on, smoking my cigar as if nothing was the matter. That put the Proctor in a bait, I can tell you! He came fuming up to me. 'What do you mean, Sir,' says he, quite pale with anger (he was a great bull-headed fellow, one of the strongest dons of his year, that's why they made him a Proctor) —'what do you mean by breaking the University Statutes in this way?' 'It is a fine evening,' said I (I was determined to keep cool). 'Do you mean to insult me?' said he. 'No, old boy,' said I, 'I don't; have a cigar?' He couldn't stand that so he called up his bull-dogs. 'I give him in charge!' he screamed out. 'I'll have him sent down!' 'I'll send you down first,' said I, and I just gave him a push—I never meant to hurt the fellow—and over he went. I rolled over a bull-dog to keep him company, and, as the other fellow didn't want any more and stood aside to let me pass, I finished my stroll and my cigar. 'Was the Proctor hurt, Sir?' inquired a small boy with great interest. 'More frightened than hurt, I always said,' said Mr. Tinkler lightly, 'but somehow he never would proctorise any more—it spoilt his nerve. He was a good deal chaffed about it, but of course no one ever knew I'd had anything to do with it!" '

"Now that is as typical and as true as any such account can be. The one weakness which is common to us all is to attribute to ourselves stories and actions which in fact do not belong to us. Of course Mr. Tinkler had never met a proctor in his life, but I'll wager that he told that tale so often that he believed it implicitly."

"Did not Shakespeare have the same thought when he wrote Henry V's speech before Agincourt?" asked Gresham.

Old men forget; yet all shall be forgot
But he'll remember, with advantages,
What feats he did that day.

Mr Tinkler as it seems, gave a liberal interpretation to the advantages."

"Precisely," replied Prendergast, "and there is no shadow of doubt that the same thing goes on to-day. Imagine the ex-Rhodes Scholar giving advice and recounting his reminiscences to the newly elected Rhodes Scholar in, say, the Middle West. Does he tell him whose lectures to attend or where the Engineering Laboratory is situated? Certainly not; he tells him how he led the proctors a long chase from Botley to Magdalen and how he put the Dean on the top of a bonfire after he had helped to take his College boat to the head of the river. Of course there's no truth in any of his stories. I've no sort of doubt that half the exploits of most of us here should be more truthfully attributed to other men. The law of evidence——"

"Is not within the scope of your lecture," hastily interrupted Tennant, "but carry on."

"Well, I remember a good few riotous nights in my youth, and I half believe now that I was the central figure in them all, but no doubt that's a later gloss. And I remember bump suppers and youthful orgies and hoaxes. I suppose really there were not very many of them, but in retrospect they seem to have happened every other day. And what fun they were! They are the days that live in my memory!"

"Historians seldom relate," said Waterlow dryly, "the accounts of those occasions when authority triumphs. I recall one famous occasion when a great disciplinary officer surveying a quadrangle filled with riotous undergraduates pronounced with almost magical effect the single magisterial sentence—'Let those who can put those who can't to bed'."

"What was the most hectic day in your life, Winn?" asked Tennant.

Winn had been paying very little attention to the conversation for some time and he hardly appreciated the turn which it had taken, but he made an effort to bring his mind back to the subject at issue.

"Didn't Oman write something about the most stirring days in his long life?" he asked. "I feel sure he did, and that he had chanced to be present—or to assist as the French would say—on a great number of historic occasions. Yes, I feel sure he did. I remember, though, that one night I asked two eminent scholars what had impressed them most in their lives, and they both gave the same answer; it was the sight of Garibaldi in the streets of London— let me see, that must have been in '64 or '65. Very remarkable that the same incident should strike them both as being incomparably impressive. I suppose it was a triumph of personality combined with a wonderful appearance, for I cannot think that Garibaldi had any qualities of the mind which would have commended him to learned men. It is remarkable, though, how the personality of great men impresses itself upon the generality of persons who really know little about them. The Bishop of Rhodesia—North Rhodesia or South Rhodesia, I really cannot remember—no doubt I shall later—the Bishop anyhow was a Paget and he told me that when he was a child in the Deanery Mr.

Gladstone came to stay with his parents. His nurse, so he told me, was a staunch Conservative and thought of Mr. Gladstone as a kind of arch-fiend, though I'm sure that a Conservative to-day would think much more kindly of him. Do you think that politics to-day are as bitter as they used to be? Of course there are these dreadful Communists. Now what was I saying? Oh yes, of course. Well, the nurse told the children that they must be polite if they saw Mr. Gladstone because he was their father's guest, polite but frigid; then when the evening came she concealed them behind a curtain on the staircase so that they could spit at Mr. Gladstone as he went down to dinner—without being seen. I'm not quite sure if it was very nice to put ideas like that into children's minds."

"I'm sure that that's very interesting," said Tennant, "but we mustn't digress too much, and the Senators will not expect us to discuss political animosities with them. We were talking, you know, of great occasions when authority was flouted or when the University was hoaxed in some memorable way. Remembering that the guide-book should include the time-honoured chestnuts, I must think that we are in honour bound to begin with Calverley and the Master of Balliol. 'There are the windows of the Master,' he said to the visitors whom he was showing round Oxford, 'and now,' he went on after selecting a large stone from the ground and hurling it through the glass, 'now, unless I am greatly mistaken, we shall see the Master himself.' "

"I trust that in our capacity as guides we shall not repeat that experiment," said Gresham. "I remember a similar story which was current in my day. It was a period when the mock funeral was fashionable; when a man was sent down his friends would arrange an elaborate funeral procession from his College to the station, with a hearse and mourners and every kind of ribald accessory. One undergraduate, after a long career of unpunished crime, was unfortunate enough after a bump supper to hurl a firework which struck the Head of his society who was surveying the scene of revelry. The undergraduate was sent down next morning and, as he was a man notorious for waging a kind of guerilla warfare with his College Dean and with the proctors, everyone expected that a mock funeral of gigantic proportions would mark his departure from the University. Everyone was in the streets; the proctors with their bull-dogs were on the *qui vive*, but to the surprise of all the culprit went away quietly in a hansom cab and stepped into his train. When, however, his friends returned to their College a neat little gravestone was seen in the middle of the grass in the quadrangle and on it was inscribed the initials of the undergraduate, the date of his academic demise and beneath them the words from Acts XXIII: 'I wist not that he was the high priest'. I'm bound to say that that seemed to me amusing, ingenious, and quite harmless."

"Precisely," exclaimed Prendergast. "That is exactly why this subject fascinates me. It's the fine line which has to be drawn between rags and hoaxes which are amusing and those which are not. We all like ingenious ideas, and we all have a fellow-feeling for the adventurous youth who flouts authority and gets away with it, but we all detest anything which involves cruelty or bad taste. It ought to be easy to know into which category any particular action falls, and yet it is often immensely difficult. This is exciting, dangerous, ingenious, and at the worst a youthful extravagance which has gone rather near the line, says counsel for the defence. This is an act which no gentleman would have done—it shows lack of taste and lack of thought for the feelings of others, says the prosecution."

"Hasn't a gentleman been defined as one who would never willingly give pain to any other individual?" asked Tennant.

"Yes, but let me give you an instance where judgment is difficult. A noted leader of the Labour movement in its early days was visiting Oxford to address a large meeting in the Town

Hall. Some undergraduates who did not share his political views
went down to the railway station on that foggy winter evening
and as the bearded politician stepped from the train, wrung him
by the hand, commiserated with him on the lateness of his train
and hustled him into their waiting cab. Then they produced a
bag or sack and pulled it over the man's head; they drove a
couple of miles out of the town and deposited him in a lonely
place by the side of the road, having first satisfied themselves that
he would be able to release himself from his bonds in about ten
minutes. They then proceeded to the Town Hall in order to
refresh themselves with the sight of the meeting anxiously
awaiting the appearance of the chief speaker. But, when they
arrived and entered the Hall, they found the Labour leader well
started on his speech, and the horrid truth became apparent to
them that the bearded gentleman, who might be supposed by
then to have struggled from his bonds, was in fact an innocent
stranger."

"What happened?" asked Mitton.

"Nothing. That stranger must have been a man of unusual
character. I like to think that he surveyed the situation with a
calm and balanced mind, that he considered that even if he
succeeded in tracing his persecutors he would find it difficult to
obtain substantial damages from them, and that in any case he
would appear in a rather ridiculous light. He therefore concluded that he would say nothing at all about it. That argues
either invincible shyness or great magnaminity and self-restraint.
I prefer the latter alternative."

"I think it's a disgraceful story," said Pacey hotly. "The whole
business was got up by some pampered and privileged so-called
gentlemen. They only perpetrated the outrage because the
bearded man was Left Wing. If they'd gone to prison for it
they'd have had a damned good lesson and got what they
deserved."

"You may be right," said Prendergast, "but can you put your hand on your heart and say that you would react in exactly the same way if the undergraduates had been some of your red friends and the bearded stranger a pompous and despised old Tory? Be honest. Isn't it all a question of the point of view? When a gifted artist paints a picture which is indistinguishable from a Vermeer and deceives the experts, we all applaud and think it a first-class joke—except the connoisseurs in Holland. Perhaps the Dutchmen would have laughed the loudest if some British artist had painted a few Reynoldses or Constables. It really isn't easy. I still think that the line between, say, the amusing and the irritating is hard to draw."

"I entirely agree," said Waterlow. "We always think that in every issue there is a black and a white, and there never is. The drawing of this line is at once the most difficult and the most important operation which we have to perform. Is that the essential thing which we learn at the University—discrimination and judgment—the difference between good and bad taste? You told us, Robert, that the guide-book ought to be sententious, so I will follow out your command. Isn't the great fundamental lesson which men learn here how to discriminate between the important and the unimportant? It sounds easy and is in fact most difficult. I don't think that three or four years at a University are wasted if a man acquires that power."

"We mustn't take the Senators too far into discussions of that kind," said Tennant. "Let us stick for the time being to our simple tales. I thought myself that David's undergraduates were rather near the knuckle; the classic example of a hoax in modern times was Dr. Emil Busch's lecture, wasn't it? When an undergraduate gave a bogus lecture in broken English on psychology and deceived enough distinguished dons to make his reputation for ever."

"Yes," said Gresham, "but for simplicity coupled with artistic appreciation I liked best the action of the undergraduate who climbed the Ashmolean one night and placed an open umbrella in the hand of the statue of Apollo at the top. I well remember that Providence seemed to approve, for it sent a shower of rain out of a clear sky next morning. There's the whole difference, as it seems to me, in placing an umbrella where it appears to be exactly needed and in balancing a trophy—if I may use that word—on the top of the Martyrs' Memorial. There is taste in the one case and vulgar advertisement in the other."

"Could we not add some personal reminiscences of this kind to the guide-book?" asked Tennant. "That would carry conviction. Who can contribute a story in which he appears himself?"

To everyone's surprise it was Gresham who responded to this request. "Mine," he said, "was not the part either of the hero or of the villain in this tale, but I did participate and, I think, I can claim to have carried out my allotted task successfully. It so happened when I was a freshman that my tutor had run foul of one of the leading men in the third year—let me call him Hughes, for I must not give away his real name. He had a distinguished career as a soldier in later life, but in those days he had some trouble with examinations, and I think, if my memory serves, that my tutor had been responsible for sending him down for a term, and irritating him in other small ways. My tutor was also a man of character and parts—I shall call him Captain for purposes of ready reference. One day Hughes asked me if he was correctly informed that I took my weekly essay to Captain on Thursday evenings after dinner. I said that he was, though for the life of me I couldn't make out why Hughes was interested. 'Well,' he said, 'next Thursday you must take him a very long and a very good essay because I've got a score to settle with him, and I want your help.' I felt flattered by that and asked him what I had to do. This was the plan which he then unfolded. Captain's

rooms had a window which looked out over the Fellows'
garden, and, since the levels on the two sides of the building
were different the ledge of the window was only about five feet
above the ground. 'On the window ledge outside,' said Hughes,
'I shall plant a bomb (which I am preparing) which will be
detonated by a time fuse. Your business is to read your essay
loudly and for a long time so that Captain does not hear the
sound of the bomb being placed in position. After the explosion
you will hurry with Captain into the garden in order to see
whether there are any traces of the malefactor, for I'—and here a
wicked light shone in his eyes—'I shall, in fact, be lowered from
above by a rope to fix the bomb and shall also be hoisted into
safety after I have set the fuse. Whilst you are in the garden I
shall walk down the staircase into College in order to establish
my alibi.' Hughes was a man of adventurous disposition and
Elizabethan gusto, and he had little difficulty in persuading a
rather callow freshman to lend his aid." Gresham paused and
smiled reminiscently. "I wrote that essay and a good essay it was,
long and learned and full of contentious remarks to keep Captain interested, and on the Thursday night I took it up to his
room. The wooden shutters of the window were closed and the
curtains drawn and Captain carried out his usual routine of boiling a saucepan of milk (a practice of his which caused me
irrational irritation) and setting it beside his armchair. You may
talk of vicarious experience—I can assure you that that evening I
experienced all the sensations which must, I am sure, be those of
the goat tethered to attract the tiger. Very faintly I heard muffled
sounds which I rightly connected with the fixing in position of
the bomb; then came silence and I guessed that Hughes had been
hoisted into the room above. I confess that my diction became a
little confused and halting. 'You are reading your essay very
badly to-night, Gresham,' said Captain, helping himself to a
second cup of hot milk. Then came the explosion! This was

before the days of world wars and we didn't know much about explosives, but Hughes was a man who did not do things by halves or leave anything to chance. The wooden shutters and the curtains were blown into the room, the saucepan of hot milk splashed all over the floor, the carpet was smothered in dust and soot. My tutor reacted in a manner which I had not expected, though it was entirely in accordance with his character. 'My God,' I heard him exclaim, 'I might have been killed; they don't know how valuable I am.' 'Let us run down to the garden, we may catch them,' I exclaimed, and to the garden with a torch we ran, but needless to say there were no tell-tale footprints there. Meantime the law tutor, who lived higher up on the same stair-case, came hurrying down and showed a modified pleasure when he learned that my tutor was alive and apparently unharmed. But neither his legal brain nor the more enthusiastic researches of my tutor could solve the mystery—and a mystery it remained—even though Hughes sent a message expressing horror at the outrage from the J.C.R. Committee and an offer to turn all the energies of the J.C.R. to an attempt to discover the perpetrator of what he called 'this dastardly outrage'." Gresham smiled once more. "A mystery it remained, but I recollect that twenty years later I was dining at All Souls and heard our old law tutor, by then a professor, narrating the history of that evening. 'Then I saw a pale and hysterical little scholar,' he said, 'cowering behind the smoke in a corner of the room.' 'No, no,' I protested, 'I was down in the garden before you got down from your rooms'."

"By Jove, Gresham," said Tennant, "I had no idea that you had lived so dangerously. I feel rather nervous of asking for more personal experiences, lest the guide-book becomes a history of crime."

"I wonder," said Waterlow, "if I am alone in thinking that David's talk has not taken the turn I had expected. I thought he was going to tell us stories not of hoaxes and such-like, but of bump suppers and bonfires and the vast potations of the young. In a way I'm sorry that he hasn't, for I hold theories about that kind of thing and I should have liked to discuss them with the Senators."

"What are your theories?" asked Tennant.

Waterlow considered for a moment how he should put his case. "Perhaps the shortest way of explaining what I mean is to start with Gibbon's remark about the dull and deep potations of the old excusing the brisk intemperance of youth," he began. "But I should like to go a little further than that. Think of freshmen's wines, such as we used to have in the old days, or bump suppers, or blinds of all kinds when the young get mildly or even completely drunk on a not very plentiful allowance of liquor; how do we regard orgies of that kind? Some of us hold up our hands in pious disapproval; others murmur something about excuses of lack of experience and a few wild oats doing no harm and so forth. But why can't we be honest and say that it is a valuable and profitable experience for everyone to be drunk once or twice?"

"My dear Waterlow," protested Mitton, "you cannot possibly defend drunkenness among the young. Have you the least conception of the harm caused by the acquisition of early habits of intemperance?"

"None whatever," replied Waterlow. "But, believe me, I am entirely serious. It's not only the warning which comes from the morning after which seems to me profitable. The young man, I do believe, who is a little drunk for the first time throws off his shyness and embarrassment and sheds the inhibitions which have cramped him all his life. For the first time he feels completely and entirely free. And he's never quite the same afterwards, for he has acquired experience and feels that he can take his place in the world without feeling frightened and without the inferiority complex—if that is the correct term—which hampered him be-

fore. I can't see Leonardo or any of the great Renaissance experi-
mentalists not acquiring that particular experience or not bene-
fiting from it. Besides, tell me, Trower, if you were back in the
Army and were, let us say, a company commander again, with a
tough job in front of you, would you feel more confidence in
all your blameless plaster saints or would you feel glad that you
had a certain number of experienced toughs alongside in time of
crisis?"

"I think that if there's a real crisis the bad hats are apt to show
up rather well, whatever they've been like before," replied
Trower.

"Yes, I think that's the usual experience. I don't want to seem
cynical, but I do feel that experience in all sorts of conditions is
almost always worth having. It's your virtuous but inexperienced
recruit who is apt to lose his head when most you need his support.
There's something in the old test—the best man to go tiger-
shooting with."

"All that is specious argument," retorted Mitton, "but I do
protest with all the earnestness at my command against your
defence of drunkenness among the undergraduates."

"No, not drunkenness," replied Waterlow sweetly, "say rather
brisk and occasional intemperance."

Tennant thought it time to intervene. "I'm sure," he said,
"that there are two sides to this question as there are to most, but
I'm equally sure that John's heresies must not find a place in the
guide-book. Whatever else we do we must not allow ourselves
to fall into an argument with the Senators about the history of
prohibition or the crimes of bootleggers. Life is too short for that.
So, with respect, the editor will suppress the Waterlow speech in
favour of moderate (or should I rather say occasional) drunkenness. It's pretty late, too, and I think we ought to put off the rest
of our discussion till tomorrow."

CHAPTER VI

"IT will not be right if we give the Senators the impression that Oxford life is only a series of riotous evenings or even of meetings of literary and artistic clubs, still less only the home of sports and amusements," began Tennant, who had been looking through his notes during the day. "To get a fair picture we ought to say more about the work of the men and about the advancement of learning. Let's start with that to-night. A day or two ago one of you said that there were three prominent features in our academic life—lectures, the weekly visit to a tutor, and examinations. I wonder if that is a fair picture."

"If you remember the importance of science in the modern world you must add the work in the labs," Pacey objected.

"Perhaps we should, but that seems to me to be common to all Universities, and we want to show the Senators the institutions and practices which are peculiar to Oxford. Of course lectures are common to all Universities too, and so we can pass them over lightly. I sometimes wonder if they are as important as some people suppose."

"I'm sure they are of very small importance," agreed Prendergast. "How many subjects can be better studied by listening to lectures than by reading books? I answer, none. It's true that idle men think they can pick up enough knowledge by attending an occasional lecture to gain a veneer of education, but all solid intellectual advance comes through reading. It's the ability to gain knowledge of a subject—of any subject—from books that is the best gift a University education has to offer. I believe that a man who has been properly grounded in, say, ancient history, or indeed any Arts subject, has acquired the power of briefing himself from books. If, for example, he accepted a post in the cloth industry he could educate himself from books on all that was essential in that particular sphere. Isn't that the answer we've been looking for? A University education makes a man fit to take up any post because his brain is trained and adaptable."

"No," said Waterlow, "that's only partly true and therefore essentially false. I agree that most subjects are better studied in books than from lectures, but it is still true that for certain kinds of instruction the lecture is the most effective vehicle. As I see it, a lecturer can do three things: he can in a broad survey give a background for specialised study; he can, if he is a very learned man, give his audience information which has not yet found its way into print; and can also indicate the sources, especially the more obscure, where further information can be found; thirdly, and most important, he can stimulate his pupils and excite interest in a way which no book can do. You will observe that neither the invention of printing nor that of wireless has destroyed the art of lecturing. Don't despise lecturing: that's easy but unprofitable. Besides, if you condemn lectures and lecturing you are declaring that our whole guide-book method is mistaken. What are we giving to the Senators except a series of lectures on carefully selected topics? Think of our digressions—they'd be hopeless in a book, but they are the essence of a good lecture."

"I agree that the most important office of the lecturer is to excite and stimulate his hearers," said Gresham. "When I was young we used all to attend the lectures of the then Master of Balliol on Political Science, and very good they were. When he passed on from a discussion on slavery in the Greek City State to an account of a slave farm in more modern days, his description was so harrowing that a coloured gentleman fainted from horror and was carried from the Hall."

Waterlow laughed. "I remember that tale being told in Christ Church," he said, "when by chance the Head of a House was dining as a guest. He was a man noted for his anecdotes, and un-willing to let any story pass uncapped. (11) 'That,' said he, 'is nothing. One coloured man fainting! In my own lecture this term two men have had fits already.' This seemed to be a sort of challenge, and Christ Church was not without its champion. 'And that again is nothing,' said an elderly don, whose father before him had also been a don at the House. 'When my father lectured, inter-collegiate lectures had not yet begun, and my father lectured to Christ Church and Magdalen men only. One morning as the lecture began one of the Magdalen men fell down in a fit; his companions gathered round him, thrust a piece of india-rubber between his teeth and bore him from the room. My father was anxious about him and therefore walked down to the Lodge to see if the sufferer had been safely conveyed to his own College. When he returned he found to his great annoyance that the room was empty. At his next lecture my father reproved the Christ Church undergraduates for their behaviour. "Sir," said one of them, "our absence is to be explained thus. When you left the lecture room one of our number, overcome by the distressing spectacle which we had just witnessed, also fell to the ground in an epileptic seizure. We thought it best to remove him before you returned, so that you should not be saddened by this second disaster." So you see (came in triumphant crescendo) my father could give two men fits with one lecture.' "

"I trust," said Prendergast, "that the Senators are not liable to fits."

"Probably not," replied Tennant, "but perhaps it is as well that Mitton proposes to speak on the New College windows rather than on the sufferings of Cranmer."

Gresham interposed a little shyly. "Are we not treating this matter of lecturing a little lightly?" he asked. "Surely John Waterlow was right when he told us just now not to despise it. I find it almost humiliating to confess that nothing clarifies my own mind like delivering a lecture. Even in our discussion on the guide-book I have found time after time that through the necessity of stating my view, I have been able to clear my mind on matters which before had filled me with doubt. I can write those dubious and hazy sentences which leave my meaning obscure both to my readers and to myself, but when I speak I am, I hope, much more explicit. But perhaps I am singular in this—really I do not know."

"You may well be right," said Tennant, "though clarity is not perhaps the highest virtue. Does not the original thinker—Adam Smith, for example—seem to go round and round in circles just because he *is* an original thinker and is in hot pursuit of the truth? It's the second-rate expositor, the publicist, the pedlar of other men's ideas, who is clear-cut and convincing. Besides, is the benefit of the lecturer himself the end which we have in mind? Granting that delivering lectures is an admirable medicine for the lecturer, is it so certain that it is equally beneficial to the patient, or impatient, audience? But we won't spend too much time on lecturing, for after all it is the hours spent with a tutor in discussion which is the essence of Oxford teaching. Let us turn to that. Stephen Leacock made that clear once and for all."

"You mean when he talked of an undergraduate being smoked at by his tutor?" asked Waterlow. "I think that the passage is worth quoting, if, as I expect, the book is in our library. Yes, here it is. 'I understand that the key to this mystery is found in the operations of the person called the tutor. It is from him, or rather with him, that the students learn all that they know; one and all are agreed on that. Yet it is a little odd to know how he does it. "We go over to his rooms," said one student, "and he just lights a pipe and talks to us." "We sit round with him," said another, "and he simply smokes and goes over our exercises with us." From this and other evidence I gather that what an Oxford tutor does is to get a little group of students together and smoke at them. Men who have been systematically smoked at for four years turn into ripe scholars. . . . A well-smoked man speaks and writes English with a grace that can be acquired in no other way.' There's a great deal in all that. In retrospect I find it difficult to recollect precisely any hour spent with my tutor, yet I'm convinced that most of what I learned as an undergraduate came from those hours. The conversation, even if it strayed from the matter at issue, started ideas and made me think. Any mind, and especially the young mind, needs sharpening on another. You don't arrive at truth by listening to lectures, still less by hearing debates or discussions—that contention for the last word is the bane of all human relations. No, no—the more I think of it the more do I feel that the private hours, as we used to call them, with a tutor were the kernel of our Oxford education."

"I can't go all the way with you," said Tennant. "Isn't it true that the constant reading and discussion of essays leads to an over-emphasis on criticism, and that criticism is the real enemy of the constructive artist? If you are for ever criticising you will never achieve anything. (I admit that harm is done to the teacher rather than to the pupil, but that is not an adequate defence.) Surely it's better to produce something, even if it's jejune and imperfect, than to refine and polish and criticise and amend and end with nothing accomplished. The search for perfection is, no doubt, a chastening experience, but it's not production—or so I think. My own recollection is that, on the whole, I derived more benefit from one or two papers which I wrote for undergraduate societies than ever I did from the talks I had with my tutor. It was the feeling that I was myself creating something—feeble though it might be—that encouraged me—and I did feel, too, that in my fashion I was trying to arrive at truth."

Gresham nodded in acquiescence. "I should go a little further even than that," he suggested. "Discussion with a tutor and the

THE TUTORIAL, from the painting by Edward I. Halliday

mental discipline that comes from talking with one of greater experience than oneself are no doubt advantageous, but isn't it true that the greater gain comes from that easier and freer discussion and argument which goes on unceasingly among the young. Let me read you a note on that subject which I had from a friend, for he puts the point better than I could.

" 'The main part of an undergraduate's education is imbibed from other undergraduates. One may indeed acquire from lectures or laboratories the rudiments of a subject in which one wishes to specialise. But the processes of higher education are subtler; it is a question of what gives the stimulus to the creative or logical powers and of the mode by which the mind makes a transition from the commonplace to the mature outlook. This higher education has to provide our society with men capable of initiating new thought, whether in letters or in science, and with men who, by the breadth and mellowness of their understanding, will be capable eventually of valuable leadership in statesmanship, commerce, and industry.

" 'It is the general testimony of those who have achieved distinction in these various fields that they learnt more of permanent value from their fellow-undergraduates than in any other way. There are the societies for debate and discussion, and there are certain traditions which the older generation of undergraduates hands on to its successors. Part of the tradition is a certain mode of frankness in discussion. The half-formed thought in a young mind may easily wither, smothered by the conventional platitudes of the market-place. At the University it is not allowed to die; it is drawn out, developed, and tested in argument, so that each young man acquires self-confidence, and therewith the power to develop his gifts. The technique by which this is achieved—more ancient than the psycho-analyst's sofa—is peculiar to undergraduate life; it consists in a certain subtle blend of flippancy and intimacy. Then there is the clash of opinion. It is *de rigueur* in the University atmosphere to pretend to understand the merits of the opposite point of view; one ends by really doing so, and thereby becomes an educated man.

" 'The dons form a background for these vital processes. They form a good background, because, although they may often be old-fashioned and crabbed in their general views, they are revolutionaries in their own subjects, no matter whether it is a question of splitting an atom or displacing a comma in an ancient text. Thus the pupil who receives instruction is made conscious of a dynamic world of new discovery, and of the fundamental insecurity of established orthodoxies. He gets a glimpse of the processes by which new truths are arrived at. It does not matter that dons are often poor teachers, for the aptitude to research, which is their fundamental business, may not be conjoined with the teacher's flair'. (12)

"That all seems to me to be finely said (though I'm not certain that I agree with the final sentence), and surely the writer holds the scales even. It is fair to praise our tutorial system, but we should never forget that undergraduates learn most from their fellow-undergraduates. Perhaps I am really only underlining and expanding the view which David propounded when he said that the papers he had written for societies of which he was a member had helped him more than any formal or informal instruction that he had received. Besides, I've another and more fundamental criticism to make of our tutorial system."

"And what is that?"

Gresham twisted his fingers together and seemed to have difficulty in finding words to express his meaning.

"I think," he said after a pause, "that I must put it in this way. The world has become so hurried and so insistent that the pursuit of learning has ceased to be a leisured pursuit bringing its own reward and has become instead a breathless chase after material rewards. I'm putting it badly, but Winn at least will grasp my meaning. Everyone now bends his energies towards the attainment of, let us say, a second class or some such label because he has been told that he must have at least a second class to obtain an appointment in the Civil Service or in some great business or in a school. The young man of to-day becomes the slave of examinations, and he loses, or so I think, the heaven-sent chance of becoming a really educated and cultured man. You're partly to blame, Mitton. When I go to chapel I always try to join in all the prayers, but there's one moment when I draw the line."

"You amaze me," said the Chaplain. "I own that I am at a loss to think what part of our liturgy can possibly offend you."

Gresham smiled. "It's when you have that prayer for the University and College and pray that true religion and useful learning may abound, my dear Mitton. I hate that phrase. True religion by all means, but it is *useless* learning that I want to see flourishing. Useless, that is, in the judgment of the generality of persons. Of course I know that no learning can really be useless, but I do protest—as you would put it—with all the earnestness at my command, against this pursuit of learning which is directed towards a definite and material end. Why can't scholars read for the love of reading and study for the pure delight of knowledge? That's what all the truly great scholars have done, and it's that that we've lost. But I'm sorry to speak so warmly—forgive me."

"I'm interested and impressed," replied Tennant, "but as editor of the guide-book I have to consider the progress of that great work, and I must admit that I think that we ought to pass on to the other topic connected with work at Oxford. We agreed, did we not, that lectures and tutorials and examinations were the three topics that we should ask the Senators to consider. I suggest that we pass to the subject of examinations. We know that Gresham doesn't like them, but what do the rest of you think?"

"No, no, one moment, please," protested Waterlow. "I'm not

satisfied about this at all. Gresham has put forward a truly contentious view, and we ought to discuss it. Let the Senators wait! At any rate, I'm going to have my say about this topic. It seems to me, Gresham, that you are in danger of dropping the bone out of your mouth as you watch the reflection in the water below. Of course it's desirable that men should study for the love of learning, but if you press your argument too far you are—as I think—in danger of changing, and spoiling, the University. If only those are encouraged to come here who wish to study for the love of study and to read for the love of reading without any thought of future employment, then only one type of student will come here. A good type, yes, but still only a type. We're all agreed that the purpose of the University is to bring together every sort and kind of man; we want, we must want, to bring here not only the scholars and the men of learning, but also those who will govern our country and control our Empire and fill our professions and spread our business (and with it our good name for honesty and integrity) over the world. That's not hot air, it's sheer common sense. If you want men of that type you must make provision for them to be trained and taught. If you will the end, you must will the means too. It seems to be fashionable to appeal to Mitton, so I'll venture to ask him to preach to us soon on the parable of the talents. It wasn't only the ten-talent man who was commended. I'm not at all sure that it's Gresham's first-class pupils who gain the most from their time here—they'd probably be first-class men anywhere and always."

"I protest," Gresham interrupted. "Surely I made it clear that I dislike those artificial labels of class. It's not the so-called first-class man that I am concerned with, but simply the lovers of learning and the followers of truth."

"True," Waterlow replied. "I've misrepresented you, but I don't think that my argument is affected. Ought not the tutor to pride himself more on the honest and industrious men of virtue whom he has guided safely into the second class, or even more, perhaps, on the low and dubious third whom he has saved from disaster, and in whom he has implanted some fugitive seed of learning or intellectual interest which may blossom in its own good time? And think of all those politicians and officials and such-like—of whom I've seen enough—how much better, how much more useful many of them would have been if they could have sat at the feet of Winn or Gresham or even my humble self for two or three years. Do you really think that all those peace treaties and such-like that we've watched in our lifetime would have been so ineffective if all the treaty makers had studied the history of Europe—and of America for that matter—for an honours school at one of our Universities? Ignorance is the greatest of all dangers; if only our masters in every country could *study*, what might the world not be saved?"

He glanced, almost unconsciously, at his own empty sleeve. "Yes, I'm sure I'm right. It's knowledge and experience that our masters lack. Some students may study history, for all I know, for sheer love of truth and with no other aim, but the majority should study it for the great mass of vicarious experience that they gain from it. I'm sorry to be so vehement, but I can't help it—forgive me."

Waterlow seldom spoke seriously, and Tennant was conscious of a faint embarrassment. So, too, was Prendergast, who tried, and successfully, to switch the conversation into a new channel.

"My criticism of the tutorial system," he remarked, "is once again a different one. To me it seems that it offers too much opportunity for the idle but enterprising man to get away with it. A weekly essay can provide all, and more than, an intelligent and diligent man needs to occupy his mind, but it is equally true that an ingenious and, well, not very diligent person can put together enough in a few hours to satisfy a not over-exacting tutor and spend the rest of his time on less profitable pursuits. I fancy that

I am not the only one amongst us who has been astounded by the number of different activities that a freshman will plunge into —generally at the expense of his work."

"But isn't it right that he should?" enquired Tennant. "John has put in a plea for all sorts and conditions of men; I should like to defend a variety of interests. They're not all waste of time."

"The real waste of time," asserted Pacey, who was becoming visibly irritated at the turn which the conversation was taking, "is in athletics. What a mass of nonsense is talked about the Boat Race and the Rugger match! If you could abolish competitive athletic contests, you would solve your problem of time-wasting at once."

It was Trower's turn to show annoyance.

"If you want," he began in his most aggressive tone, "to turn this place into a breeding-ground for school-marms——"

Tennant laughingly interrupted him.

"I think that the place of athletics in University education is a separate question, and I don't think that that topic was in David's mind. What exactly were you thinking of, David, when you spoke of those activities which impede work?"

Prendergast laughed. "With my usual precision I was alluding in the first instance to the three great claims on undergraduate time. In ascending order of iniquity, I should place them as religion, politics, and acting. When I hear that a pupil of mine has taken up religion, I shrug my shoulders; when I learn also that he is busying himself with politics and the political clubs, I tremble for him; when, in addition, a rumour reaches me that he is plunging into the dramatic world, I give up all hope."

"I do not think, Prendergast, that you should be so cynical," said Mitton. "It shocks me that you should consider an interest in religion to be on a par with an interest in politics or acting. Surely we should encourage all right-thinking men to concern themselves with religious thinking."

It is doubtful whether Mitton derived much comfort from Prendergast's answer. "Ah well," he said, "I'm inclined to agree with you that one vice is quite a good thing for any young man; it's when he multiplies his vices that I begin to be worried."

"I'm sorry," interjected Tennant before Mitton could continue the debate; "but really I must insist now that we pass on to examinations. Who would like to speak first on that topic? I'm supposing that Aristotle, or perhaps Porson, will ask us why examinations play so great a part in Oxford life. For they do, you know. Have you ever met an Oxford man for the first time who has not made some reference to his schools or his viva?"

"As I ventured to criticise examinations in general," said Gresham, "I feel in honour bound to declare that, if examinations there must be, then those at Oxford are probably the fairest and most reasonable that can be devised. It seems to me odious to impose on men an examination in which every answer is separately marked and the totals added up in order that each man may be given a place—that must lead to cramming of the worst kind and, incidentally, to results which do not represent the true merits of the candidates. An examination held at the end of a man's University career, designed to discover what he knows (and not what he does not know) and to put him in one class or another does appear to me to be a reasonable procedure, especially where the better men are concerned. If you study a subject for three years without examination, you cannot well (if the questions are properly set) cram at the last moment and hope to achieve good results. At least I hope not. But you can give evidence that you are a $\varphi\acute{v}\sigma\epsilon\iota$ first-class man. That procedure, compared with the elaborate lists of marks through each year which an American student produces, should impress Porson, and should give him some idea of what the Oxford system is. I hope that I'm not going back on my expressed view about the examination system. I reaffirm my belief that men should come to the University for the love of learning. Incidentally you said, David, that we should discuss the work of the men and the advancement of learning to-night, and I wanted to interrupt you and say that the two topics, far from being parts of the same subject, were in fact destructive of one another. But I must not interrupt my argument, for it's difficult to be clear and explicit. I should like, then, to see the University as a place of learning, where learning was honoured for its own sake, where those came who loved it, and where the lovers of truth and knowledge pursued their studies without any thought of their ultimate objects or of positive results. Still, I realise that that ideal is impossible, and I recognise that some sort of examination is necessary at the end of a man's University course in order to give him a qualification for his career. The ugly economic fact obtrudes itself; we have to admit that a man cannot expect to receive an appointment nowadays unless he can produce evidence of his capabilities. That being so, the competitive examination is inevitable. So far as Oxford was concerned the system started, I believe, in the very early years of the nineteenth century, under the influence of Cyril Jackson, Dean of Christ Church. Before the examination statutes of 1802–7, all examin-ations in Oxford had been a farce—for candidates chose their own books and their own examiners. But observe that an Arts degree (if I may employ the modern and convenient appellation) is not, and should not be, only a measure of a man's knowledge and power of assimilation. The head of a great business firm does not ask Oxford to send him someone well-trained in the details of commercial law or in the economics of large-scale business; the Foreign Service does not require a man who can glibly chatter in colloquial Russian or French. Those things are added to them afterwards in the course of their careers. Even the lawyer, Pren-dergast, may, I surmise, be the better in the long run for an educa-tion in some broader department of human knowledge. Surely what the potential employer requires is the well-trained brain—

a good mind which has been developed by study. I well remember a stocking manufacturer coming to me and asking for someone to draft into his business. 'What sort of man do you want?' I said. 'A first in Greats,' he replied. 'I've never been to Oxford or to any other University, but they tell me that the first in Greats is the man with the best brain. I can teach him all the technical knowledge he requires, provided he has a keen and an adaptable brain.' He may have been aiming rather high, but his theory was surely right. Very well then, that's how I look at the Honour Schools; they sort out men in degrees of quality. We know, all of us, the distinction between an honours man and a pass man. The latter can work up, by endeavour and concentration, one subject after another, and be examined in each of them in turn. Don't think that I despise the pass man—no man can be a more useful citizen, within his limits—but he's not capable of mastering and controlling comparatively large spheres of knowledge at the same time. The honours man is, and he must be prepared to write about and discuss those things which he has learned during his three years' course. Or let me put it another way. The knowledge he has acquired is the material on which he works; he applies his trained mind to mould and adapt this material. And there we come to the distinction between first- and second- and third-class men. The third-class man may just regurgitate what he has imbibed from his tutor and from lectures, but the first-class man does much more. The sign of the first-class man is distinction of thought; as we were saying the other night, the real sign of ability is the power of discrimination, the sorting out of the essential from the unessential—of the important from the unimportant."

"Isn't all that rather academic?" enquired Pacey. "I very much doubt if there's any real distinction between a first-class and a second-class man except that one knows more than the other."

Gresham shook his head. "I'm sure there is a real difference," he said, "and my own view is that nowhere in the world is that distinction better realised or more carefully shown than in Oxford. Examining is an art, and an art that has been brought to a high level here. Nothing, I think, gives to an examiner the same confidence as his first marks meeting—I mean the meeting where he reads out to his brother examiners his list of marks, and finds, almost invariably, that among two or three hundred candidates his marks tally in an overwhelmingly large number of cases with those of the others. The different classes stand out with an almost cruel clarity. But you've got to avoid those specialised questions which can best be answered by reference to some recent learned article; the wide and general questions give the man of quality the best chance of showing his merit. If you set specialised questions of the type I have mentioned, you will, in fact, only test the amount of information which a man has absorbed, and not the quality of his mind. I find all this difficult to explain, but I see quite clearly that I can reconcile my dislike of competitive examinations with my admission that they are a necessity only on the supposition that they are examinations of the proper type. I do not think that it matters what subjects you examine a man in provided that you give him an opportunity of showing the quality of his mind rather than an opportunity only of showing how much information he has acquired."

"I think I can meet you there," said Waterlow. "There is a fine speech of Macaulay's on the Government of India delivered in 1833, where he defends the plan of filling up all vacancies in the Civil Service by competitive examination. Let me quote some sentences of it to you.

" 'Whether the English systems of education be good or bad is not now the question. Perhaps I may think that too much time is given to the ancient languages and to the abstract sciences. But what then? Whatever be the languages, whatever be the sciences, which it is in any age or country the fashion to teach, the persons who become the greatest proficients in these languages and these sciences will generally be the flower of the youth, the most acute, the most industrious, the most ambitious of honourable distinctions. If the Ptolemaic system were taught at Cambridge instead of the Newtonian, the Senior Wrangler would, nevertheless, be in general a superior man to the wooden spoon. If, instead of learning Greek we learned the Cherokee, the man who understood the Cherokee best, who made the most correct and melodious Cherokee verses, who comprehended most accurately the effect of the Cherokee particles, would generally be a superior man to those who were destitute of these accomplishments. If astrology were taught at our University, the young man who cast nativities best would generally turn out a superior man. If alchemy were taught, the young man who showed most activity in the pursuit of the philosopher's stone would generally turn out a superior man.' "

Gresham nodded thoughtfully. "I agree with much of that, and I think it explains why no harm was done, but rather good, when the curriculum of University studies was confined within narrow limits and in effect to the classical authors. But I wish that Macaulay had gone further and said that the competitive examinations should be a test of quality of mind and distinction of thought rather than of acquired information. Is it, I wonder, a sign of progress or a sign of retrogression that there is a tendency to make appointments nowadays not as a result of exhaustive written examinations but after long interviews and psychological tests and such-like?"

"No," said Tennant firmly, "we shall not discuss the value of psychological tests—that might cause too much argument, and it is not really relevant. We must confine ourselves to Oxford examinations."

"Well, in that case I think I have said all that I need," answered Gresham. "Except perhaps that we must be cautious lest a School in Oxford which has existed for a long time becomes stereotyped and lends itself to stock questions and stock answers."

It was Pacey's turn to laugh. "I was told that at Cambridge," he said, "Paley's *Evidences of Christianity* was a set book for some examination or other for a hundred years, and that everyone learned it off by the use of a rhymed summary. A lot of it was quoted to me once, but I can only remember a few lines. Two ran something like this:

> '*The disciples then,*' *goes on old Paley,* '*continued in the Temple daily:*
> *Washed in the blood and free from sin, shows the good state that they were in.*' "

"I do not think," said Mitton a little stiffly, "that my worst enemies could accuse me of a lack of humour, but I confess that I consider such lines on such a subject to be in doubtful taste."

"It is curious," interjected Tennant with a view perhaps of saving Pacey embarrassment, "that any mention of blood is considered of doubtful propriety, and yet the word 'bloody' has become by slow degrees in modern homes the most overworked word in our language."

"Stranger still," added Waterlow, "that the word which brings no sort of surprise to us in a modern book comes as a shock when one meets it in, say, a classical work. Reading *Middlemarch* the other day, I almost dropped the book when I came upon this sentence. 'It would have been better if I had called him out and shot him a year ago,' said Sir James, not from bloody-mindedness, but because he needed something strong to say.' Does the eminent lady's use of that phrase offend your taste, Chaplain?"

"No doubt she used the word in a somewhat different sense."

"No doubt. Yet the phrase has an oddly modern ring. Let me try you once more. Would your taste have been offended or your sense of humour tickled by the famous misprint in the obituary on one of your own cloth?"

"I have no idea to what you refer, so I cannot reply," answered Mitton cautiously, and indeed suspiciously.

"The subject of the obituary," said Waterlow, "was an eminent cleric who died, as you would say, full of years and honour. In his obituary attention was drawn, among his other virtues, to his admirable tenor voice with which he would delight his friends and parishioners. Especially so, the account continued, by his spirited rendering of that fine old English song 'Oh, ruddier than the Clergy.' Well, Mitton, which wins—taste or humour?"

"I think it depends whether the misprint was intentional or fortuitous," suggested Gresham, who never really enjoyed the facile sport of chaffing the Chaplain. "May I not continue my remarks about the theory of examinations?"

This time, however, Tennant was adamant.

"The answer," he said, "is no—or rather, if I may soften the blow, 'the editor regrets'. You know, I am beginning to realise that an editor's life is a hard one, especially for a soft-hearted man. I think that, like an effective Prime Minister, a successful editor must be a good butcher. I hate to say it, Gresham, but you have indeed already exceeded the space allotted to you. Esteemed contributor though you are, the editorial blue pencil must now be brought into action to bar your further progress, but I promise you that you shall be allowed to address the Senators on this particular topic, and that you shall have the first opportunity of proving to them that, bad in essence though examinations are, Oxford examinations are the best examinations that have yet been devised."

"But what about the viva?" said Prendergast. "It's the viva which is still the distinguishing feature of Oxford examinations and the feature also which is still most warmly criticised and most hotly defended. Does the guide-book lend its authority to the viva or not?"

"True," said Tennant, "we must throw that bone of contention to the Senators to gnaw. Winn, what is your opinion? Is the viva a good thing or not?"

Winn had for some time paid little attention to the discussion. It was a warm evening, he was pleasantly tired, and he had, in fact, been asleep for some time. The word 'viva', however, roused him, and he adjusted his pince-nez in order to give due weight to his answer.

"Indeed," he said, "I have the greatest respect for the viva-voce examination, and all the Presidents of this College whom I have known would, I am sure, have agreed with me. They used to take the greatest pains to examine the young men orally when they were candidates for admission to St. Thomas's. Let me see. Old Fothergill, but of course he was never President, and Eccles and Vereker and Hatfield—all of them quite admirable. Never pompous, you know, but friendly and approachable. It's really very hard for me to decide which of them was the most skilful at interrogating candidates. When I say that they were never pompous I do not for a moment suggest that they lacked dignity —far from it, but they knew how to combine dignity and courtesy with easy accessibility. Yes, perhaps old Fothergill was really the most skilful and effective of them all, but of course, as I said just now, he was never President of the College, though there is no harm now in saying that he might have been had he so wished. A remarkable man, greatly gifted, and yet modest and retiring to a fault. But really I cannot answer your question—I do not think that you should ask me to compare one President with another—really I think that that would not be quite proper on my part."

"But perhaps you could with propriety tell us whether you think the viva itself is a good thing or not," suggested Tennant.

"Of course I could," replied Winn. "That is a simple and straightforward question. I can answer it best, I think, by considering the questions which our Presidents used to ask candidates when they first came here. They did not always get the information they sought, though. I remember one occasion as accurately in every detail as though it had occurred yesterday—very amusing it was, too. Let me see, was it Eccles or Vereker who was President then? I really can't remember, though I ought to be able to. It must have been Eccles, I think, for he was certainly in Holy Orders—but, dear me, Vereker was in Orders too. How tantalising, I cannot imagine how I can find out which it was."

He paused, and seemed to regard the subject at an end.

"Perhaps," suggested Tennant, "you could refer to him as the President, and tell us the story, all the same. You had said, you know, that the President did not always get the information he required or the answer he expected when he was interrogating a candidate for admission."

"Ah yes," said Winn; "how good of you; I think that will get me out of my difficulty. We were all seated at the table in Senior Common Room interviewing the candidates in turn. A young man was alone on the other side of the table, and the President was asking him questions in the usual way. I was struck, I remember, as I often had been before, by the skill with which the President put the young man at his ease. He had asked him all about his studies at school, and what books he had read, and what his interests outside the schoolroom were, and what school he was proposing to read at Oxford. Finally the time came when the President wanted to find out what plans the candidate had for his career after he had completed his course at the University. So he said to him . . ." Winn paused and a light of triumph appeared in his eyes. "Of course it was Eccles and not Vereker," he announced. "Both were affable and courteous and unembarrassed, but Vereker was much more precise and, indeed, fastidious in his choice of words than Eccles. Vereker would *never* have made such a remark in precisely those terms."

"But what was this famous remark?" asked Pacey a little impatiently.

"The President—or Eccles as I may now refer to him—said, 'And what about the future life?'," Winn chuckled. "And the candidate replied, looking tense and suspicious, 'I hope to go to Heaven, Sir'. The President was very put out, I remember, for some time by that reply."

"I enjoyed the story," said Tennant, "but I'm still not clear if you think the viva a valuable part of an Oxford examination—for that is the topic which we shall have to be prepared to discuss with the Senators. For my own part, I think it to be an essential as well as a traditional part of a degree course and I'm ready to advance arguments in favour of it which seem to me incontrovertible, but I should like to know if all of you share my views before I put them into the guide-book."

"I can never forget my own viva in Divinity Moderations, or Divvers as we used to call it," said Gresham. "The examination, much to my regret, was abolished in the early 1920s, but everyone had to take it before that. At one time it was an examination in the Thirty-nine Articles, but in my day we were examined in two of the Gospels in Greek and the *Acts of the Apostles* in English, and of course there was a viva-voce examination. It was the first University examination which I underwent, and I well remember that I prepared myself for it with the utmost care. Perhaps the College rule that scholars should be fined £5 for failure acted as an incentive to my assiduity. Be that as it may, I am sure that when I attended for my viva I knew the *Acts of the Apostles* as thoroughly as any young man of nineteen can ever have known them. There were half a dozen of us in the room waiting for our turn, and a sprinkling of curious spectators as well; I was the second on the list and I watched the first victim, if I may so describe him, with friendly yet critical interest. Perhaps, I thought, I may gain some useful hints about deportment

"WE PAUSE FOR A REPLY," from the painting of a viva voce examination by
S. P. Hall

and demeanour from him—I shall observe perhaps what sort of behaviour makes a favourable impression on those hard-faced elders who sit on the other side of the table.

"The first candidate appeared to me rather older than most undergraduates; grave and composed, he seemed to radiate dignity and wisdom. Almost, I felt, the examiners should apologise for subjecting such a one to this elementary test.

"'Where, Mr. X,' asked the Chairman, 'was St. Paul born?'

"A long pause followed; evidently the candidate was considering the question in all its bearings; finally he replied confidently.

"'Ephesus, Sir.'

"The Chairman shook his head, and posed another question.

"'Can you tell me, Mr. X, to what place St. Paul was travelling at the time of his conversion?'

"This time the pause was even more prolonged. I had the feeling that the whole roomful of people was trying to force the correct answer into the candidate's mouth. He alone retained his composure and with bowed head warily considered his answer. At length he looked up and replied, though with a little less assurance.

"'To Ephesus, I believe.'

"A second time the Chairman wearily shook his head, and asked yet another question.

"'Where, Mr. X, was St. Paul shipwrecked?'

"This time the tension was almost unbearable. Sometimes in the summer the whole sky seems to turn black and one feels as though a thunderstorm must burst, and still there is a horrible and sinister delay. So it was then. The candidate, looking wiser than ever, seemed to be applying all his faculties to the task of answering the question. Every resource of that powerful intellect was devoted to solving the problem submitted to it. Everyone in the room, too, seemed to be fighting on the side of the candidate. The pause and the silence became almost unbearable; I was biting my lips to prevent myself from shrieking out the answer, and yet I knew with horrible certainty that the disaster was inevitable. And so it was. At long last the candidate made his decision.

" 'I think, Ephesus,' he said.

" 'Thank you, Mr. X, you may go,' said the Chairman, and long before I could recover my equanimity I was seated at the table. Somehow the first question appeared to come to me from a great distance: 'Mr. Gresham,' said one of the other examiners —for I suppose that the Chairman had exhausted his repertoire— 'Mr. Gresham, can you tell me where the goddess Diana was worshipped?'

"I felt, I remember, that some horribly subtle and ingenious trap had been laid for me; I must on no account fall into it. So I sat silent and tried desperately to make sure that I should give the desired answer. The pause seemed to me like eternity, and I fear that I must have wasted almost as long as my predecessor. I could feel the tension in the room, and I could imagine the eager faces of my companions sitting behind me. Finally in a voice so low that I fancy the examiners can hardly have heard me I murmured timidly:

" 'Was it not Ephesus, Sir?'

" 'Thank you, Mr. Gresham; it was, and you may go.' "

"An excellent story," said Tennant, "but again I'm at a loss to know if you are testifying to the value of the viva or not. Each of my expert witnesses, you and Winn, has told an agreeable tale, but I really don't know whether the evidence has been given for or against the viva. So far as the guide-book is concerned I shall follow my own inclination unless anyone raises an objection. The viva, I shall say, is an integral part of the Oxford system; the arguments in favour of its retention are weighty and obvious; those in favour of its abolition for the most part specious and frivolous. If the Senators show fight and demand a discussion,

Winn and Gresham will tell their tales and, unless I am much mistaken, by the time they are completed the Senators will have no fight left in them. Seriously, though, have we dealt adequately with this subject of work in the University? David, you and Trower are our practical men; is there any obvious question which a Senator will ask us, and which, so far, we have ignored?"

"I think there is," replied Prendergast. "There is the obvious question—do men work more than they used to? It is almost universally believed that in the bad old days no one worked, and that nowadays men work so much that they miss all the other advantages which they could obtain from Oxford. If Samson or Aristotle really plans to send a son here, that is the first question which one of them will ask. How will the guide-book tackle that question?"

"The orthodox answer is clear enough," replied Tennant. "Without going further back in the history of higher education we can say without fear of contradiction that in the eighteenth century the University was a play-ground for the well-born and well-to-do, learning was neglected, and the whole place was corrupted by idleness and drunkenness; in the nineteenth century, partly no doubt owing to the influence of competitive examinations, the standard improved; but at the beginning of the twentieth century Oxford was still the monopoly of a class. Then came the first war and a period when men, trying rather pathetically to revive the pleasures of a bygone world, came up for a few terms to decide on their futures and to forget the horrors of a four years' war. Then finally the second war and a period when the University was thrown open to all who were intellectually worthy to come here and when the undergraduates devoted themselves to steady work and honest endeavour. We have got to admit, I think, that no generation has been more worthy of this place than the present, or has better used its opportunities."

"If that is the orthodox answer," protested Gresham, "I submit that it is misleading and, in some respects, quite untrue. I will admit that no generation which I have known is more worthy of respect than the present, and that this may well be due in large measure to the fact that opportunity to come here is now afforded to all who can reach a certain intellectual level. But to my mind, in order to praise the present generation of men, it is not necessary to denigrate their predecessors. The remarkable thing about different generations of undergraduates is not their differences but their similarities. There have always been diligent men and idle men, clever men and obtuse men—and there always will be. Besides, my belief in freedom makes me distrust the uniformity of the present age; there may be, there probably are, more men who deserve and receive a sound second class. I doubt if there are more with a real spark of genius, or more who are capable of attaining to the first class. I should like to challenge the orthodox view all along the line. I might even be moved to attempt a defence of eighteenth-century Oxford."

"Then please do, if you will be reasonably brief."

Gresham considered for a moment in order to arrange his argument.

"I think," he began rather haltingly, "that my sympathy for eighteenth-century Oxford is based to some extent on my dislike of examinations, but of course I must not base my defence solely on the fact that there were no serious examinations then. Nor must I try to prove too much, for I am inclined to agree with Wordsworth (13) when he says that Cambridge, though she must yield the palm to her senior in the seventeenth and nineteenth centuries yet on the whole was more productive and more vigorous in the eighteenth century than Oxford. I think I will try to make two points and two only; the first is that in fact much more useful work was done than is popularly supposed; the second that the products of the system did much to justify it.

"The generally accepted view, then, is that in eighteenth-century Oxford the professors did not lecture, the tutors did not teach, the undergraduates did not work, and that all these classes vied with one another in a contest of idleness and dissipation. Well, here is the account of the daily life of a student at the beginning of the century, written in Latin by one Benjamin Marshall, but you'll allow me to read it in translation:

" 'I rise before dawn, and at six o'clock attend the public Latin prayers. . . . After breakfast I go for a walk with my friends; we talk together and stir one another to jocularity and laughter, in fact mingle serious things with play. In this way, after the lapse of half an hour, our walk is finished, I return home, and from that time shut myself up in private. There I occupy myself with the study of the Minor Prophets, with the Latin commentaries . . . upon them. . . . The next hour I take in hand the poem of Togrœus (?), and I work at him till nine o'clock. From nine to ten I give my mind to Philosophy, which that Roman orator deservedly calls a kind of progenitrix and parent of all the arts which are worthy of praise. . . . When it strikes ten I go to my tutor, Mr. Pelling, a man indeed thoroughly learned in all the liberal arts, and no less polished in the elegance of his Latin. He expounds some portion of philosophy to me and my friends until eleven o'clock, at which time, as you have long known, the bell calls us to luncheon ("*prandium*"). Luncheon finished, I go with my friends to Kuphipolium [Kuphifolium?] as it is called (apparently a coffee-house). There, amongst ourselves, we discuss public affairs. . . . In this way time goes on till one o'clock, when I return to my rooms and gird myself for my studies. I apply myself at once to the Koran, a book which, like almost all others, you, learned Sir, know extremely well. . . . Over this, then, I employ myself until four o'clock. Then, at last, I place Aristotle's *Rhetoric* before my eyes, a book indeed worthy of having an author so great as was that truly wise philosopher of Stagira. . . . I turn over, then, the *Rhetoric* until six o'clock, at which hour, as you well know, the bell calls us to dinner ("*ad cœnam vocat Tintinnabulum*"). After dinner I either go to bed and read the *Odes* of Horace or the witty epigrams of Martial, or mix with my friends in a sociable way until nine o'clock. Then, when "Great Tom goes" ("*sonante Clusio*"), we are all glad to go to Latin prayers. Nor is this an unpraiseworthy custom; for in the morning we pray for success upon our doings, and in the evening we return thanks for such success as has been secured.' (14)

"That does not sound like idleness to me! And it is, I submit, as a picture of the life of a studious undergraduate strictly relevant to the purposes of the guide-book. You may, however, think that deterioration set in as the century advanced. That perhaps would be the natural inference to draw from the experience of Adam Smith (though he became a good Greek scholar at Balliol) or of Jeremy Bentham, who thought '*mendacity and insincerity*' the natural results of a University education. The chief witness, however, who is always quoted—and whose prejudiced and bitter words on this subject are seldom questioned—was Gibbon. Everyone knows his account of the teaching provided at Magdalen in his day and of the lives of dons and undergraduates of the time. Yet of the thousands who have read and reread their Gibbon, how many have paused to consider that Johnson is a far more reliable witness, and how many again have known of the existence of (and far less perused) James Hurdis's (15) vindication of the University of Oxford, and of Magdalen College in particular, from the posthumous aspersions of Mr. Gibbon. Consider the facts. Gibbon was matriculated before he was fifteen, and he stayed a bare fourteen months; of this five months were spent on vacation, and six lengthy excursions to London and elsewhere also interrupted the short time of his academic life. He was indeed a child plunged into a great academy whilst he was still deficient in the qualities and attainments which might have made him capable of deriving benefit from an Oxford career. His diatribe on the teaching in Magdalen will not, surely, bear examination. Hurdis's account of the tasks imposed upon Magdalen undergraduates and of the degree of proficiency expected from them is formidable indeed (I will not weary you with it), his defence of the Magdalen tutors and of their lectures is to me convincing. But I must not pause too long over James Hurdis except to urge you to read his pamphlet. If you get nothing else from it, you will enjoy his defence of the type of conversation to be expected in a Senior Common Room. For my part, I believe that the idleness of eighteenth-century Oxford has been much exaggerated; it may have been true that the professors lectured less often than they should have done, but I believe that the efforts of the College tutors have been much depreciated. John Wesley declared that he would have thought himself '*little better than a highwayman*' if he had not lectured on every weekday in the year. '*Whenever a young man becomes Jorden's pupil, he becomes his son*', said Johnson of his tutor. Indeed, the list of good tutors through the century is a long and honourable one. Nor can I believe that all the undergraduates failed to seize their opportunities of acquiring learning—some surely used those opportunities to the full. Then as now there were idle men and industrious men, and not a few who were betwixt and between.

"Of course there were! And that brings me to my second point, the results or the products of eighteenth-century Oxford. It's not my business to construct a defence of the eighteenth-century governing classes. I'm only concerned with one side of their lives—in fact, with the intellectual. Now, I suggest that whatever else may be urged against them the eighteenth-century statesmen and politicians were at least as highly—and as well—educated as their twentieth-century successors. In scholarship and classical learning they made a brave show. I need not go through the century searching for examples, though indeed I should have no difficulty in finding a multitude of witnesses. Let me confine myself to the younger Pitt and to Charles James Fox—the one educated at Cambridge, the other at Oxford. As I read Pitt's career at Cambridge, he is the model of the industrious student; never, except when prevented by illness, did he fail to attend morning and evening chapel; never did he spend an evening without the College walls. It is true that, as the son of a noble-man, he took his degree without examination. (Don't snort, Pacey. It was illness which compelled him to take advantage of that privilege.) No doubt he could have passed any examinations with ease and distinction. He went to acquire learning, and he surely acquired it. But, on the whole, I think the example of Charles James Fox will aid me more. There was a great scholar, who loved learning for its own sake! I know all the arguments which can be advanced against him as a man and as a politician, but that cannot prevent me from admiring him beyond all his contemporaries for his generosity and his human qualities. Watch him prompting Pitt through a Virgil quotation in the House of Commons at a time when the rivalry of the two men was at its height. Better still read, or reread, the third volume of the *Memorials*, and learn from that how genuine was Fox's love of learning. Did not Oxford play some part in that? What is most remarkable to me is to observe how Fox's classical taste has been confirmed by later generations, especially by the scholars of our own time—but I must not develop that argument, for it is a special subject. What does strike me is the fact that the freedom of the University was well adapted for the production of such men. Is it conceivable that Fox would ever have submitted himself to a competitive examination? If he had he would doubtless have been ploughed, for he would have ignored those subjects which did not appeal to him, if indeed he ever remembered the date of the examination.

"We have to admit, I am sure, that the eighteenth century was a period of intellectual giants, whatever we may think of the state of the Universities. This is what G. M. Trevelyan says in his *Social History*. 'In spite of the decadence of the only two Universities that then existed in England, in spite of the decay of the endowed schools specially charged with secondary education, the intellectual life of the country was never more brilliant, and the proportion of men of genius per head of population in the irregularly educated England of George III was immensely greater than in our own day. It would seem that the very highest products of the human mind are the outcome of chance and freedom and variety rather than of uniform organisation.' You must remember that Trevelyan has not been sparing in his criticism of the Universities in the pages which immediately precede these sentences; indeed, he seems to accept all Gibbon's charges without question. For my part, whilst warmly supporting his conclusions, I should be tempted to go further and maintain that the intellectual advance was even encouraged by the lack of organised control in the Universities. Think of the scholarship and the literature, think of the buildings and of the pictures; think how much of all this was due to men educated at Oxford and Cambridge and then condemn the eighteenth-century Universities out of hand if you dare! No, I'm sure it was the freedom and opportunity (even if it had to be sought) which counted, and, willy-nilly, I'm back at my examinations again! All the evening I've been worrying my brain to discover where I read the best defence of my point in the eighteenth century. Well, I have remembered, and it turns out that the passage was not written in the eighteenth century at all. But it is authentic for all that."

He pulled out from the bookshelf a copy of *Let Dons Delight*.

"Now this is part of a conversation in the Common Room at Simon Magus in 1788, when the same question which the Senators are likely to ask us is being discussed. One Fellow has already complained of the drunken revels of idle undergraduates.

" '*Mr. Shillett* (who has been a Fellow for more than fifty years). They are not altogether idle, Sir. I think there is less idleness among the boys than there was formerly, when I was first a fellow.

" 'Mr. Hammond. If they are not idle, it must be their native ambition that spurs them to it. It needs very little incumbence upon their studies, if they are to answer the questions for their degree.

" 'Dr. Jennings. Good God, man, you are not for holding annual examinations, like Mr. Jebb, who has been raising such a hornet's nest at Cambridge? If you younger men had your way, I believe you would have all the men, with no respect to their station and capacity, reading themselves crack-brained for three years; and then set down to answer questions with paper and ink, whether Berkeley had the better of Locke, and whether David Hume has not shewn us a better way than either of them, and a multitude of trash besides. Sir, this is not to polish the minds of the young gentlemen; you will not make them apt for affairs by filling their heads with book learning, and giving prizes to the one that has the longest memory and the quickest wits for holding his own in a disputation. I could tell you of many men, since I became a fellow here, who shewed mighty little promise over their books, and yet proved themselves men of uncommon excellence in public life.'

"Well, you really must forgive me," Gresham concluded. "I said that I would not try to prove too much, and I fear that I have gone near to breaking my promise. But do let us be charitable, and, whilst we admit the shortcomings, admire those virtues also of a period to which we owe much."

"It was at least an agreeable age for dons," murmured Pacey cynically.

CHAPTER VII

"IT occurs to me," said Tennant, "that our yesterday's discussion will put rather a heavy strain on the Senators. Educational theory may be of absorbing interest to some of us— or at least we may be willing to have it believed that it is—but it's the personal anecdote which claims the attention of the stranger. It's vacation and that makes it reasonable to attach our tales to the Senior Common Room—besides, the Common Room is the fruitful breeding-ground of Oxford stories. I suggest that we should tell the Senators something about ourselves and our friends. To my mind, Tuckwell should be the best-loved son of Oxford, and his *Reminiscences* is the best of all Oxford books, just because he concentrates on personalities rather than on institutions or theories. It's the Oxford characters that live in the mind, even if they are characters of a past generation."

"This is the moment," Waterlow began, "when someone is bound to remark that there are no characters in——"

Mitton, however, was speaking almost at the same moment. "I have sometimes observed," he said, "that there are no characters in Oxford nowadays."

"How agreeable," murmured Waterlow *sotto voce* to Prendergast, "to escape the fatigue of completing one's own sentences. And I know exactly what the Chaplain will say next!"

"But then," went on Mitton, "I observe further that this may be a delusion, and that we ourselves, or some of us, may indeed be, wholly without our knowledge, the characters of this generation—Winn, for example." (16)

"I dare say you are right," said Tennant, "but that is only a partial explanation. The simple reason for the apparent dearth

197

of characters is surely the retiring age. It takes time to become a character. All of us have known many, but I doubt if any of us could name a young character in Oxford. An undergraduate star of magnitude—yes—but not a permanent star, only the shooting variety. I'm sure that it's survival which builds up a character. If one of us attended every Union Debate—or every University sermon, for that matter—and always sat in the same seat or pew, and always wore the same kind of clothes, he would qualify without any further exertion. How quickly, too, the legend would grow! The twenty-five years would become forty in about a week; the suit of clothes would become the original suit made in 1900. It's just survival and the passage of time which make the character. Still, I'm all for describing our Oxford characters to the Senators, and certainly no place could be better fitted than this Common Room for collecting the old stories about them. John, you know as much of Common Rooms as most men, so you shall start. You admitted a week ago that no guide-book would be complete without some of your Common Room stories."

Waterlow smiled. "I'm quite ready to do my best, but I have to remind you again that you must be suspicious when I use the pronoun 'I', for in this connection it means either my father or myself. He spoke to me so often of his own experiences in Common Room that I am now totally unable to remember, even if I wished to, whether certain remarks were in fact made to him or to me. 'I', then, in all my anecdotes means Waterlow *père ou fils*, and I refuse to be told by Pacey or by David that any consideration of dates, or vulgar facts of that kind, prove my story to be untrue. At the lowest estimate, my stories are true in the guidebook sense. Do you accept this conventional use of the first person singular?"

"Of course we do, carry on."

"Good—then I start by remarking that Robert is wholly right

198

when he stresses the importance of age and survival. Respect for seniority is, or was, one of the most distinctive and agreeable features of Common Room life. I remember the first time that I (*père ou fils*, Pacey)—that 'I' took tea in the Christ Church Common Room. I had just been appointed a lecturer, and I entered the room rather shyly. There was only one other occupant, and he a venerable figure with a full white beard which rested upon his waistcoat; he was very slowly drinking his tea and eating muffins. Or were they perhaps crumpets? As you, my dear Winn, might interpolate, I really cannot remember and that is most provoking. Muffins or crumpets? Well, after all, the point is not really significant. On a chair by his side lay his umbrella and his straw hat on which was a blue riband with the cardinal's hat in red on it in front. That, I think, in my portrait of a character, is important, for the time of year was mid-winter when ordinary folk did not normally sport what was sometimes called a 'boater'. I sat down with some embarrassment, for the aged man, though staring hard at me, uttered no word, and I, for my part, felt that it would be impertinent to open the conversation. So we sat and munched our muffins and drank our tea. Suddenly, without any warning, the veteran turned his head and his great white beard towards me and said without any introduction 'In 1848 when I was quite a lad . . .', and a series of agreeable anecdotes followed. A truly memorable opening sentence! It was only later that I appreciated the reasons for his curious behaviour. He was a member of Common Room, but not on the foundation; he did not know who I was or what was my status. If, indeed, I too was only a newly elected member of Common Room, it would be proper for him to address me first—if, however, I was on the foundation it would be my place to take the initiative, if that was my wish. Seniority and status certainly played a great part in the pattern of our lives.

"Another scene comes to my mind from about the same period.

There were two old dons, who, by reference to the University Calendar, could be found to be eighty-five and eighty-two years old respectively. One night they fell into an altercation, and I remember the fascination of listening to remarks which, I had thought, occurred only in books and never in real life. 'I give you the lie, Sir.' 'And I, Sir, give *you* the lie', and so forth (I think that in those days men used the word 'Sir' more and more the angrier they became). At length they became really offended and eighty-two, rising from the table, bellowed out, 'In any other place than this, Sir, I should horsewhip you'. Eighty-five, however, had the last word. 'That,' he said, 'was a most improper observation'; then after a pause he added, 'especially from a junior man.'

"Seniority and juniority meant a great deal to us and so did our traditional privileges and peculiarities. Casting my mind back, it seems to me that most of our number had a sort of proprietary right in certain subjects for discussion, and even in certain stories. You said earlier, Robert, that a guide-book ought to include those chestnuts which have stood the test of time. In my early days in a Senior Common Room everyone had his own stories, and it would have been considered plagiarism and bad manners for anyone else to relate them. Certainly they did not lose by repetition—indeed, we used to employ the most elaborate artifices to persuade the proprietors or monopolists to repeat their favourite tales. One don, a real Oxford character even quite early in his life, had a great reputation as a raconteur, and I used often to wonder what gave his stories their special and peculiar flavour. I came to the conclusion that they owed much to the fact that he seldom used a personal pronoun; almost invariably he repeated the names or titles of his *dramatis personæ*. With 'my uncle the general' or 'my cousin the archdeacon' the story would begin, and with those worthies and *not* with 'he' or 'they' the story would continue."

"And what was the story of my uncle the general?" enquired Mitton.

"Often though I heard it, the exact point of the story—if indeed it had one—at this distance of time escapes me. I dimly recall that the *mise en scène* was family prayers—perhaps my uncle the general was paying a visit to my cousin the archdeacon —and that the family cat, inappropriately concealed beneath the dining-room table, played a not inconspicuous rôle. My uncle the general was accustomed to use language more suitable for the camp than the rectory, and I'm pretty sure that he ejaculated 'Damn that cat' at the critical moment. Beyond that point, Chaplain, I cannot satisfy your very natural request for information.

"Then there was the Steward—like yourself, Trower, an ex-regular—who could sometimes, but not easily, be tempted or tricked into telling one or other of the tales in his repertoire. One, I remember, was concerned with a Professor of New College. The Steward met him walking down the High and wearing one black shoe and one brown. 'This, Professor,' said the Steward, 'is strange.' 'Yes, indeed,' replied the Professor. 'I have worried about this problem all day, and stranger still, much stranger, is the fact that I distinctly observed in my bedroom this morning another pair, of which one was black and one brown too. I really cannot understand it at all.' The Steward had another favourite also, of which I remember absolutely nothing, except that it bore the improbable title of 'How d'ye do, how d'ye do, said the Proctor'. He only told that one on very festive occasions, and after a good deal of encouragement."

"I don't think that the standard of story-telling can have been very high," murmured Pacey.

"Now Pacey, don't be supercilious. What stories do you and your cronies tell when you are lounging around among your test-tubes and retorts and Bunsen burners? Correct me if I misuse any of the technical expressions. Come now, can you cull from your laboratory gossip a single story which is better than that of the perplexed professor or that has a better title than 'How d'ye do, how d'ye do, said the Proctor'? If so you may tell it here and now. Ah, I thought not—you are silent and thus admit defeat. But I will tell you two more stories, which you will be unable to criticise and to which you will pay a tribute of awed respect because they were told to me by Einstein.

"Einstein, you may know, lived with us for a year before he went to America, and very pleasant it was to enjoy his society, for he had the humanity and the modesty of a great man. I only saw him ruffled once, and that was when a correspondence in *The Times* indicated that Oxford was given over to riot and drunkenness. 'A monstrous accusation,' declared Einstein; 'all the time that I have lived here I have not seen an intoxicated undergraduate.' Conveniently forgetting that the Professor invariably retired to bed at nine p.m. and did not give himself any very favourable opportunity as an observer, we bent all our energies to the attempt to persuade him himself to write a letter to *The Times* in defence of Oxford undergraduates. He would, he wouldn't, he would, perhaps he would. . . . Alas, alas, I've never ceased to regret that that letter was never written. It's true that he always protested that he couldn't speak English easily. Of course he could—but that's neither here nor there—and sometimes he would feel it his duty to contribute to the amenities of the evening by telling us a story. The human memory is fallible, but I have a distinct recollection that on such occasions he would always tell us one of two stories, and that on specially festive occasions he would tell them both. I'm sure he felt that some such contribution was expected of a loyal member of Common Room."

Winn emerged suddenly and unexpectedly from a long silence.

"Now, that is most interesting," he said, "and bears out a

belief to which I have long subscribed. I believe it to be a Continental, or at any rate a German, custom that each guest and each host shall contribute something to the evening's entertainment. Probably it was a similar convention which constrained the Victorian young lady to take her music with her when she went out to dinner. It was unthinkable, you know, for a young lady of the period of my parents not to have some social accomplishment, and even earlier, I fancy, some sort of musical proficiency was expected of every person of gentle birth. Samuel Pepys, now, and his friends—everyone was expected to be able to sing a part or play some instrument. And the Elizabethans! I've often been struck by their accomplishments. An aristocracy, you know, only survives by virtue of being an aristocracy, and the gifts and accomplishments of a cultured and intelligent minority seem to me to be of real value not only to their possessors but to the whole community. I often think that everything which is decently good in this curious world of ours derives from some privileged minority or other. How otherwise can you justify eighteenth- or nineteenth-century Oxford? No, no, you really must not condemn privilege out of hand—as often as not privilege justifies itself a hundred times over. I recall that in the Greek City State——."

A gentle but admonitory cough from Robert Tennant checked him. "Dear me, I must ask pardon, I am almost giving a lecture after we all agreed that lectures were the most unsatisfactory part of Oxford life; it is really unforgivable on my part. Now, why did I start talking at all? I'm sure that I wanted to say something which sprang directly from those agreeable anecdotes of Waterlow's."

He looked round with an air of mild but helpless distress.

"My legal training," said Prendergast, "fortunately enables me to cling resolutely to the matter at issue, and I can therefore come to your assistance. I put it to you that you were, at one time, on the verge—on the very brink—of making a comment on what you regarded as a Teutonic custom of contributing to the general entertainment in the course of a convivial evening."

"But of course," said Winn, "and how very kind of you to refresh my imperfect memory. I often think, you know, that we do scant justice to the kind-heartedness of lawyers. How often do they come to our aid in our difficulties; how often do they give us sound and practical advice. Yet if you search the portrait gallery of lawyers among the Victorian novelists, you will invariably find them portrayed as selfish and worldly and avaricious. Of course many of them, the real not the fictional lawyers, I mean, had a hard struggle and arrived at eminence from quite obscure condition. I've often wondered whether the story about Mansfield, the great Mansfield, is true or not. Perhaps Waterlow can tell us. It is said that when he came to be matriculated he was entered on the books at Christ Church as having been born at Bath because his Scottish accent was so broad that when he said that he was born at Perth he was—quite understandably—misunderstood. But we should throw no stones. To me it seems that faulty elocution is one of the scandals of the modern age, even in the Church. I remember——"

Trower, who had been growing visibly impatient, now launched a frontal attack.

"Were those damned old Huns you were talking about lawyers?" he asked.

"I have never talked of damned old Huns in my life—that is not the kind of expression I should ever use."

"I think," said Tennant, "that the Bursar only meant to ask you to tell us more about the German custom you mentioned—the custom of contributing to the evening's entertainment."

"Ah yes," replied Winn. "I was just about to do so when one or other of you, I forget which, interrupted me. It is very trying to be interrupted, and I lose the thread of my argument too easily nowadays when interruptions occur. It was really a very curious story, told me many years ago by a Fellow of Balliol, for it was in the Balliol Senior Common Room that this incident occurred. One night a Bavarian admiral was dining there. Now that was very strange. I asked at once when the story was told to me how the admiral could have been a Bavarian admiral, for Bavaria, you know, has no seaboard. My friend explained this, but I no longer recall what the explanation was. I am only sure that this German guest was in truth a Bavarian admiral. After dinner when the port was circulating the admiral suddenly rose to his feet, bowed to the Senior Fellow, drained his own glass, and said 'The Charge of the Light Brigade, by Lord Tennyson.' He then recited the whole poem, bowed again, and sat down. The Senior Fellow said 'Thank you very much,' and pushed the decanter towards him. Nothing more whatever was said. Now that all sounds most strange, but I am convinced that the Bavarian admiral was simply complying with a social convention, and thought that it was his duty to contribute in some way or other to the conviviality of the evening. Indeed, his recitation was an act of good manners and did him great credit. What do you think, Waterlow?"

"We have still to hear the stories which Einstein used to tell," interrupted Pacey sourly, for he derived little or no pleasure from Winn's rambling reminiscences.

Waterlow smiled. "You shall hear them now. Maybe they support Winn's theory about Teutonic social conventions. The first was a comparatively simple tale. There was an old and immensely rich Jew, living in Berlin, who was about to celebrate his golden wedding. He arranged a sumptuous feast and invited his sons and daughters and grandchildren and relatives to it. A discussion very soon arose about the presents which his offspring and relatives were to give him. At length one of the sons hit on a brilliant idea. 'Our father,' he said, 'has everything which a man could desire or which money could buy. It would be wasteful folly if we gave him the golden objects which are usual on such occasions. Let us instead have a volume prepared in which all our names can be inscribed in letters of gold—and this we will formally hand to him at the conclusion of dinner.' The suggestion, which had the merit of cheapness as well as simplicity, commended itself to all and was therefore adopted by unanimous consent. When the night of the dinner arrived the eldest son made a carefully prepared speech and handed the book to his father. The patriarch replied in a few well-chosen words and then rang the bell for his butler. 'Take this book,' he said, 'and lock it carefully in the safe—but first read it through and remember if anyone whose name appears in it should call, I am not at home.' "

"That reminds me," said Tennant, "of the remark of Sieyès on his death-bed forty years after the Terror. He sent down to tell the porter that he was not at home if Robespierre should call."

Gresham shook his head. "I've always thought that a disturbing story," he said. "Fear, once implanted, clings in a hateful way. I'd much rather remember Sieyès by that remark of his when, some time after 1830, he was asked by a deputation to return to the Institute, and refused. '*Enfin, je ne sais plus parler, ni—ni—me taire.*' That shows real self-knowledge."

"To my mind," said Prendergast, "Einstein's Jewish patriarch was simply administering a snub to his rather mean offspring. No doubt the snub was deserved, but it seems to me that in such matters old age has an unfair advantage—the young can hardly answer back with effect."

"That's not always so," chuckled Trower, "though now that I'm getting long in the tooth, I sometimes wish it were. I'll tell you about an answer which was given on the golf-course here. A very famous but not very good-tempered Professor was playing, and behind him there were two undergraduates. Whilst the Professor was putting, one of the undergraduates, who thought that he

was out of range, played his shot up to the green. He played an unusually good shot, and the ball had a lucky downhill fall, so it
just trickled on to the green. The undergraduate knew the Professor by sight and reputation, so he hurried up, cap in hand, and
apologised for playing too soon. Unfortunately the Professor had
been playing very badly and was in no humour to be pacified.
He entirely refused to accept the apology, suggested that the
undergraduate ought not to be allowed to play on the course, and
that his conduct was unbefitting a member of any recognised
golf club. 'But I suppose,' he wound up, 'that you cannot be a
member of any reputable golf club.' The undergraduate was
nettled. 'Sir,' he said, 'I am a member of the Royal and Ancient
Golf Club at St. Andrews—a club for which, if my information
is correct, your brother was recently black-balled, owing to
a prevalent but mistaken belief among the members that he
was you.' "

Tennant laughed. "Yes, the senior does not always score over
the junior. Still I do agree with the inference from David's remark
—the inference that the best snub is the one delivered when there
is no advantage of age. I like, for example, the tale of the eminent
cricketer at Lord's who was watching the Eton and Harrow
match. An acquaintance who met him there (and you must make
the acquaintance an Etonian or a Harrovian according to your
company) remarked in a rather supercilious tone—'I did not know
that you were at either school'. 'No, I wasn't,' replied the cricketer,
'I'm only watching the game. But now I come to think of it,
didn't I see you last year at Gentlemen and Players?' "

Pacey made another effort to assert himself. "Really, you
know," he said, "I become more and more convinced that we
scientists are the only people who have the least idea of sticking
to the subject. Trower pretends that he always keeps his eye on the
ball when he's playing games, but neither he nor any of you think
of keeping to the point. We were promised two stories of

Einstein's, and I'm still hoping, though without much confidence, that we shall hear the second."

"There's some substance in your complaint," said Waterlow, "and I shall be delighted to carry out your wishes. Einstein's second story was more subtle than the first and concerned two peasants in some country district of Germany. It was a still, warm summer evening and the peasants were walking slowly homeward at the end of a long day. All round them the frogs were croaking as they do croak on such evenings as that. One of the peasants was better off than the other, for he possessed a cow; the other was very poor. The calm of the evening or the croaking of the frogs or some such outside agency filled the richer peasant with thoughts of pity and generosity, and suddenly he turned to his companion and said, 'If you will eat one of those frogs alive I will give you my cow'. The poorer peasant did not pause to consider; he jumped into the field, seized a frog, shut his eyes, and with a few powerful bites consumed the unfortunate creature. The two friends then continued their walk. Now it was the turn of the poorer peasant to feel some contrition. This good man, he said to himself, has given to me his precious and only cow. Am I really justified in accepting so valuable a gift? Finally he could bear it no longer, and in a burst of generous feeling he exclaimed, 'If you will eat a frog alive, I will give you back your cow'. We may assume, I think, that the other peasant had had time to regret his hasty generosity. At any rate, he did not wait to be asked twice. He too seized a frog, crushed it between his teeth and devoured it. The two then continued their walk for some time in silence, but at length one turned to the other and said, 'What do you think we have gained? Each of us has eaten a live frog, and very unpleasant it was; the ownership of the cow is unchanged. I cannot quite see who has benefited'. The second peasant was unable to find an answer. Einstein, if I remember rightly, used to maintain that this story had some deep philosophical significance, but I could never ascertain just what that significance was. Perhaps I might tell the story to the Senators and invite them to hazard an interpretation."

"They will be sorely tried before they reach the end of the guide-book," said Prendergast. "Almost I begin to feel sympathy with them in their distress. Seriously, are we not forgetting our brief? As I understood it, the plan we were following was to tell them something of Oxford characters as they flourished, or have flourished, in Common Rooms—but all we have done so far is to narrate a series of stories, first told, it is alleged, in Common Rooms yet having little or no connection with Oxford life or manners. Isn't it time, Robert, for you to sharpen your editorial blue pencil?"

"I don't think so," said Tennant after a little hesitation. "You must remember that when we come to that part of the guide-book which deals with Common Rooms, we have one great advantage. It is that we can bring the Senators to this room. We cannot take them to watch the undergraduates at play as Trower would wish or working in the laboratories as Pacey might like because this is the Long Vacation, but we can bring them to our Common Room and let them see the scene for themselves. No description is needed, for they will sit at our table and make their own observations. What we do need, though, is a supply of those stories which bring Common Room life in the past vividly before their eyes. Besides, it's the stories which make the old characters live—or so at least I think. Strangers may believe that dons in their secluded and sheltered lives spend the evenings in abstruse and brilliant conversation about the right and the good or the latest emendations in the text of Euripides—in fact, three-quarters of the conversation which goes on here is concerned with personalities and amusing stories and sport and modern literature and trivialities of all kinds. So it should be, for this is our home, where we relax and enjoy ourselves without feeling the shackles of responsibility, and so too, I fancy, it always has been. An under-graduate's Oxford life is short. Ideas change and traditions grow up and die or disappear very quickly in Junior Common Rooms, but Senior Common Rooms are the home of lasting tradition—it's in them that the essential Oxford flourishes, and it's in them, if anywhere, that the secret of Oxford is to be found. Moreover, in my judgment, these apparently irrelevant stories give the flavour of the place more surely than chapters of description or analysis. So I say let the anecdote flourish and let us chatter to the Senators without uneasy thoughts of what David calls 'our brief'. Down with pomposity, say I, and down with our exaggerated sense of what is expected of us, but long live irrelevance, long live gossip if it be not malicious, long live irresponsibility! The editor will certainly not exclude these harmless tales. Tell me, Bursar, if you had to relate to the Senators on their first evening some characteristic Common Room story or even just some Oxford story to indicate to them the nature of our society and our habits of thought—what would be your choice?"

Trower grinned. "I've no doubt that I could find plenty of good stories if I thought awhile," he replied, "though some of them might not pass the censor. I think I'd begin by telling them something about sport just to show them that we don't confine our conversation to high-brow arguments and dry-as-dust con-troversies. And of course I'd take care to stress the fact that St. Thomas's was a place of religion as well as of education." He bowed ironically to Mitton. "How's this for a start? When I first came here I acted as Treasurer of the Boat Club, and I used to help in an amateur sort of way with the coaching. The eight wasn't going too well and so I consulted old Cannister about it, for he was supposed to have been something of an oar round about the period of the Flood. You probably remember Cannister, Winn?"

"Of course I do. He was librarian for nearly fifty years and only died about 1915. He collected the parish magazines from all the parishes in Oxfordshire and Bucks, and never realised when he put them into the Library that inside the cover all the magazines had the same contents. Summer and winter he always wore his old green greatcoat that had been through the Crimean War. It was always said, you know, that he lost all his money in trying to produce champagne in Somerset. Of course I remember Cannister; whatever made you suggest that I had forgotten him?"

"I didn't," retorted Trower gruffly. "Well, Cannister was supposed to know about rowing, and so I asked him for advice about the eight and what I ought to do to improve it. His answer came without the slightest hesitation. 'You should exclude all High Churchmen from the boat—they always insist on fasting on Wednesdays and Fridays, and that is fatal. The last time the boat fell into the hands of the High Church party, we went down six places.'" (17)

"After that, you ought certainly to speak next, Mitton," said Tennant. "You must surely be able to find for the Senators a story with a better moral than Trower's."

Mitton was plainly uncertain whether he was being teased or not, but he thought it wiser not to take umbrage.

"For my part," he said, "I should like to recapture for them something of the old-fashioned Oxford, when life was less hectic and when the vacation was truly a vacation, and not as it is now a time of extra and often unrewarding tasks."

Tennant laughed. "I must admit that you score there, though I protest against the guide-book being described as unrewarding. Still, I agree that it is appropriate to recall the older and more carefree life—when, for example, all the work of the Registry was done by one half-time official, and all University correspondence was done in long-hand. But I interrupt you—go on."

"This experience did not fall to me," said Mitton, who prided himself on sticking closely to the facts, "nor even, Waterlow, to my father [Really, thought Tennant, Mitton is acquiring some skill in irony and innuendo], but it did happen to a dear friend, now for many years a Bishop of the Established Church. I can vouch for its truth. My friend, then in his fourth year and an ordinand, was invited by the Head of an Oxford College to spend a fortnight of the Long Vacation with him in the country living to which he was wont to retire as soon as each vacation began. On the Saturday night after his arrival my friend expected his host to retire to his study in order to prepare for his Sunday duties—for, though he showed not the slightest interest in the village during the week, he was a conscientious man (18) and preached morning and evening every Sunday. On the Sunday morning he still appeared to make no preparations until the bells were ringing, nor indeed until the rectory clock stood at a quarter to eleven. He then turned to my friend, saying that it was time for church. They walked together into the hall and the rector opened the lid of a great oak chest which stood there, and into which he plunged his head and shoulders. From behind my friend was able to observe that the chest was almost completely full of manuscripts, all neatly rolled up and tied with pink ribbon. The Rector plunged his hand deep among them, drew out one at random and walked on to church. When the time arrived for the sermon he mounted his pulpit, cleaned his glasses and carefully untied the pink ribbon. He then looked at the first sentence of his manuscript, nodded with obvious pleasure, and said in a loud voice, 'Ah, Absalom, I perceive'. He then preached an admirable sermon on that unfortunate young man. But what an inappropriate discourse he might have drawn from the chest! I shudder to think what might have happened."

"You shudder easily," growled Trower. "I should like to know, Tennant, in what sort of way Mitton's story points a better moral than mine. It seems to me to indicate nothing but a low standard of industry among the Edwardian, or possibly the Georgian, clergy. Eh?"

"I don't think it does," Tennant replied, "but I'm sure that we needn't debate that point. Moral or no moral, it will help to give the Senators a picture of a past Oxford when life was simpler and the tempo less hurried. A clerical Oxford, too—what are you laughing at, Gresham?"

"It's only the phrase '*a clerical Oxford*'. For some reason that brought back a picture to my mind. I see the old Provost of my College hurrying—as always, almost but not quite late—to chapel on Sunday, buttoning his surplice as he goes. And I hear his beautiful but throaty voice as he gives out the notices. 'Wednesday and Friday of next week' (and here he clears his throat and tries, but without success, to read his own notes) 'Wednesday and Friday of next week will be, will be . . . Wednesday and Friday.' How like him, and characteristic, I think, of those days. We all knew what he meant, and it was agreeable, as it were, to see his mind working."

"Exactly," commented Tennant, "in cases of that kind you can watch and appreciate the other man's mental processes. Do you remember that headmaster famous for his forgetfulness? An old boy once asked him that most unfair of all questions, 'How are you, Sir? You don't remember who I am, do you?' 'But indeed, I do,' replied the headmaster, 'I remember you very well, but, let me see, was it you or your brother who was killed in the war?'"

"A good story," said Prendergast, "but in my submission it should be ruled out of order, because it has no Oxford connection. If I had to explain the Oxford mind, or rather the Senior Common Room mind, I should be tempted to narrate the tale of the philosopher who married."

"Do," said Tennant.

"He was a brilliant and forceful teacher and, if my memory serves, very much beloved by his pupils. Was he at Magdalen or Balliol? I cannot now be sure. In his teaching he adopted the method of the Socratic dialogue, and he was also a peripatetic philosopher—by which I mean, Trower, that he was wont to take his pupils for long walks—four miles an hour and all the afternoon—what time he and they wrestled with the great problems of philosophic doubt. The *mens sana*, as Mitton would say, was cultivated in its *corpore sano*. Then one day the philosopher married and walked with his pupils no more, for he walked with his wife instead. But old customs are hard to change and the dialogues continued. One day an old pupil met his master, striding as of yore along a country road, and as he passed him the conversation, as he affirmed, ran something after this sort. 'That, then, is my thesis; to it you might be tempted to object that' (and a long sentence followed); 'but I should then immediately reply' (and the rest was lost). A yard or two behind the philosopher walked, or hurried, his devoted wife."

Waterlow smiled. "I agree," he said, "that that is a good Oxford story, but I was trying earlier in the evening to tell Common Room stories, and I fancy that I can recall one at least which will give the Senators a good picture of the behaviour of members of a Common Room in their hours of leisure. I recall, for example, that even when I (or perhaps my father, Mitton) had recently joined the Christ Church Common Room it was decided by my seniors that we should enter for the prize poem on a sacred subject. You enter, you know, under a motto, and send your name in in a separate envelope. The arrangement was that each person who participated was to write twenty, or maybe thirty, lines, and that he must take over where his predecessor stopped."

"And I suppose you will tell us that the Common Room won the prize," said Pacey. "I can't say that I'm altogether surprised, for the judges in those things don't always inspire confidence."

"No, not quite," Waterlow replied. "No doubt the poem ought to have received the prize, for the men who wrote it were

a group of highly intelligent and gifted scholars, but I'm bound
to confess that the composition (and that's surely the right word)
was a little uneven. One contributor, I remember, hard put to it
to complete his quota, produced the majestic line

One, two, three, four, five, six, seven, eight, nine, ten.

He said that this gave, better than any other line in the language,
the impression of horror and suspense, but some of us doubted
if the Professor of Poetry would properly appreciate it. There
were some truly poetic passages though:

His gentle heart his cruel purpose mocks.
Do not soft conies dwell in stony rocks?

Yes, I feel sure that we deserved the prize, even if it was awarded
to some less worthy competitor. What impressed me, though,
was not the quality of the poem but the enthusiasm with which
the Common Room threw itself into what was, after all, just a
light-hearted and amusing interlude. I realised then that men
take an infinity of trouble over trifles and are much more serious
about trivialities than about their real work. That, I think, is the
secret of mental relaxation and perhaps, in a way, the secret of
our Common Room life."

"The *jeux d'esprit* of professors will be remembered long after
all their learning is forgotten. I shall always remember a bishop
who dined one night in Common Room, and next whom I sat.
Over the soup his conversation, in which I did not take the major
part, was concerned with some philosophic niceties in the works
of the Early Fathers. As the evening wore on, the bishop unbent
more and more. Of his early remarks I remember nothing, but
I treasure his farewell utterance—for it was a *cri de cœur*. 'Ah,' he
said, slowly shaking his head, 'had I but known that spades were
trumps, I should have played the hand far otherwise!'"

Tennant, like the careful editor he was, was studying his notes, and he now intervened in the discussion.

"I asked at the beginning of the evening," he said, "for some typical Oxford and especially Common Room stories, and you've all been good enough to contribute. I'm sure we have enough to start the evening going, for one tale will lead to another, when the Senators are actually sitting with us here on Wednesday. I suggest, therefore, that we pass on to another section, or even another topic."

Surprisingly Gresham raised an objection. "I don't want to delay you unnecessarily," he said, "but I do think that, if the guide-book aims at including the most characteristically Oxonian stories, it ought to find room for the tale of the tortoise at Corpus."

"You mean Oriel," said Pacey, who was not averse from correcting his seniors if opportunity offered.

"No, I mean Corpus. The Oriel tortoise is an historical character, but it belongs to a later age. The story of the Corpus tortoise was told me—more than once—by the Provost of my old College, and I should dearly like to see whether the Senators would appreciate it. But I had much rather that Winn should tell it, for he would do it more justice than I could."

"I'm sorry," said Winn, "but I really cannot recall that I have ever heard of the episode which you mention."

"Then you must bear with my imperfect rendering—though I wish that some of you had heard the Provost himself tell it, for he contrived—or so I thought—to find just those words which were needed to turn a simple little anecdote into a memorable saga. Understand, then, that many years ago there lived and flourished two dons, brothers, one of them at Corpus and one at Worcester. The object, or one of the objects, of the story was —so I was led to believe—to draw a clear distinction between the characters of these two brothers. One of them was the original from whom the portrait of the tutor in *Verdant Green* was drawn, a fact which will enable historians to date my little tale. I shall call them Richard and Edward Gracey, though those were not their names. Richard Gracey of Worcester was universally liked and respected; Edward Gracey of Corpus was a great scholar, but apparently opinions differed about his personal qualities. (At this stage the Provost would pause, and gravely remind me that I must be careful to remember that this was the brother of the other Gracey and consequently not the prototype of the tutor in *Verdant Green*.) For some reason the personality of Edward Gracey became a burning and contentious question among the undergraduates of Corpus. How and why do such idle controversies originate? I cannot tell, nor indeed should any prudent person dogmatise about the why and wherefore of undergraduate opinion. It is sufficient to record the fact that the whole of Corpus—not a large but a highly intelligent body of men—was divided on this single issue. Had Mr. Gracey a sense of humour, or had he not? The Junior Common Room was racked with dispute and argument, friendships which had endured for half an undergraduate lifetime were broken, the affairs of the College, and indeed of the nation, were neglected, and still the question was unsolved. The minute book of the College Debating Society showed that there had been a record attendance on the occasion when the President's casting vote had to be given on the motion 'that, in the opinion of this house, Mr. Edward Gracey lacks a sense of humour'. It seemed indeed that Corpus would be permanently divided into two equal, hostile and irreconcilable camps, for the idlest controversies are usually the hottest and the most difficult to resolve.

"Then one summer day Mr. Gracey sauntered after luncheon through the College garden, and there observed some undergraduates who were trying to persuade a reluctant tortoise to extrude his head and eat a dandelion which they held before him.

For some time Mr. Gracey watched the scene in silence; then he remarked, 'Why don't you try the other end?' and walked on without waiting for a reply. For a brief spell it seemed as though the great problem was solved and that peace and unity were at last restored to the College. Alas! the event was otherwise, for as the news of Gracey's mot spread the controversy burst out again with redoubled bitterness. On the one hand, it was vehemently argued that this epigrammatic utterance showed conclusively that Mr. Gracey need not fear comparison with the brightest wits of his, or any other, generation; on the other side, it was stoutly contended that he had offered only a piece of practical but humourless advice. A meeting of the Debating Society, specially convened, carried the matter no further, for the distracted President found it necessary once more to exercise his casting vote on the motion 'that, in the opinion of this house, the episode of the tortoise proves conclusively that Mr. Gracey possesses a keen sense of humour'."

"And how did it all end?" enquired Mitton.

"That," said Gresham, "is precisely the question which I asked the Provost, but he gave me, as I seem to remember, an indirect or even oblique answer. A twinkle appeared in his eye—a sort of slow twinkle which I could almost describe as a wink. 'I hope,' he said, 'that I have made it clear that the Gracey of my story was *not* the tutor in *Verdant Green*. You must learn to discriminate very carefully between the two brothers.' "

"I call that rather a feeble yarn," said Trower. "The Senators won't get much amusement out of that."

"It occurred to me," replied Gresham, "that we might learn from their reactions something about their own sense of humour, and that we should then be able to judge whether they were competent to enjoy the special flavour of Oxford stories. But I may be wrong."

Tennant hastened to forestall any rejoinder from Trower.

"I was wrong just now to suggest," he said, "that our primary task to-night was to collect Common Room stories. Did we not really intend in the first instance to select some Oxford characters, and ought we not now to describe some of them for the benefit of the Senators? They could be living characters, if such exist, or characters of the past—that is immaterial—provided only that they represent something worth remembering in Oxford life. Whom ought we to begin with, Winn?"

Winn considered for a short time before he replied. "I am sadly perplexed," he said at length, "for it is most difficult to make a choice which will commend itself to everyone. Routh of course was a great figure—Burgon included him, you will remember, in his *Lives of Twelve Good Men*—perhaps he would be the best to choose. Unless, indeed, you are of the opinion that Jowett is more representative of modern Oxford thought."

"I did not really contemplate going quite so far back," said Tennant. "It seems to me that we should confine ourselves to men that some of us have personally seen and known. But your mention of Routh and Jowett does suggest to me that we should open up a rich mine if we started with Heads of Houses. We could run through all the Colleges and describe the more memorable Heads of each with whom we here have been acquainted. Let's start with one of the Colleges on the perimeter—Magdalen or Keble or Worcester or Pembroke. Surely we shall find characters there as interesting and as *outré* as the most avid of Senators could desire. Winn, you begin—and choose any College you wish, except, of course, St. Thomas's."

"Well," said Winn, "it is very difficult to decide which College I should be right to choose, for I have had friends at all of them. I think I must choose Magdalen, for I have had the great honour and pleasure of acquaintanceship with four Presidents of Magdalen, and I believe that I could find something of interest to say about each of them. The first who was President when I came up was the great Herbert Warren, though he was then, of course, quite a young man."

*　　*　　*　　*　　*

It was long after midnight and Tennant and Winn alone were left in the Common Room.

"I really feel a little uneasy, Tennant," said Winn, "about this evening's conversation. You know, we have discussed all these Heads of Houses, living as well as dead, with what in retrospect I feel to be very dangerous freedom. I feel nervous about it all. Really, if some of the stories which were told to-night were made public we should lay ourselves open to opprobrium—or even perhaps to most unpleasant legal proceedings. That is too horrible to contemplate. I had no idea, when I started to speak of the Presidents of Magdalen, how the conversation would develop."

Tennant laughed. "Don't be uneasy, Winn, I can assure you that there is no need for anxiety. David Prendergast is a good lawyer, and his knowledge of the intricate byways of libel and slander is profound, but I'm not trusting even to him. You've seen me taking notes here every evening to assist in the composition of the guide-book, but you did not notice that I tore the notes of our last hour or so to-night into very small fragments. To make assurance doubly sure, I shall put a match to them now."

He struck a match and set alight the little pile of pieces of paper in the large ash-tray beside him. "It's sad, though," he murmured, "for some of those stories were good ones. Old Hearne would have appreciated most of them, especially that tale of the Master of University who opened his front door too hastily, and I fancy that Samson would have chuckled more than somewhat over that almost indecent account of——"

"Oh, pray, no, Tennant," said Winn, holding his hands over his ears.

CHAPTER VIII

"THIS is our last evening," said Tennant, "and we must make the most of it. We have to feel reasonably confident that we can answer, or at least parry, any question which the Senators may ask us. Do you think that we have neglected any really important side of Oxford life?"

"Yes," replied Waterlow. "We have consistently side-stepped the main issue—I mean the Colleges and College life. We all agreed that the College system was the essential feature of Oxford, and the feature which differentiates it from other Universities (Cambridge, of course, excepted), but we have never discussed the merits of the system nor indicated those peculiar and subtle differences which distinguish one College from another."

"Would not such fine distinctions be wholly beyond the comprehension of our guests?" asked Prendergast.

"I think not. You will probably find, for example, that in America (and elsewhere for that matter) the reputation of Balliol for scholarship stands far above that of any other College. That, no doubt, is a legacy from the days of Jowett. I've no doubt that Balliol stands as high as ever it did, but many people here will agree that other Colleges, St. Thomas's among them, now rival Balliol in learning and in academic successes. Has there not been a levelling up—and I mean a levelling up and not a levelling down—of Colleges in our own lifetime? Reputation, however, is usually a generation or two out of date, and I should be surprised if the Senators were not keenly interested in the comparison of different Colleges. But before we discuss them, we must clear our minds about the merits of the College system itself."

"I thought we had settled all that," said Mitton. "Was it not

221

agreed by acclamation that Winn should show the Senators over St. Thomas's, and that they should be spared a visit to other less fortunate places, except when special features, such as New College Chapel, were to be shown to them? Surely our responsibility ends there, for a thorough examination of St. Thomas's will teach them all they wish to know about the internal organisation of any College, and no cicerone could act with quite the same enthusiasm as Winn or with even comparable qualifications for the task."

"That is true enough," said Tennant, "and I'm sure that Winn will need no prompting and no preparation. None the less, John is quite right, in my judgment, in insisting that we ought to tackle the theory of the College system, and explain its excellence before we give the Senators the pleasure of inspecting St. Thomas's under Winn's guidance. I suggest that we follow the same procedure that we adopted in the case of the University. Let's ask David to give us another of his legal disquisitions (with that brevity which becomes him so well). Let him tell us—or rather the Senators—what the Colleges are and what the College system is. Then we can meet their criticisms before Winn embarks on his personally conducted tour. What do you think of that suggestion, Winn?"

"I have no objection, my dear Tennant," said Winn a little stiffly, "though I can hardly imagine that these American gentlemen will find anything to criticise in our arrangements at St. Thomas's. I should have thought that a walk through the College, during which I could indicate the chief architectural and artistic merits and tell them something of the College history—especially, perhaps, the fourteenth and fifteenth-century period of our first foundation—would have sufficed. But of course if Prendergast wishes to speak in the manner you describe, I shall raise no objection."

Tennant realised that Winn was hurt by the suggestion that

anyone except himself should speak on his own chosen subject, so he attempted to correct the impression which he had made.

"I had not intended that David should intrude on your preserves. My idea was rather that he should discuss the College system generally and without reference to St. Thomas's. These Senators are very modern, you know, and somehow I don't see them imitating the Queen of Sheba when our St. Thomas's Solomon shows them the glories of our Temple—unless their questions have been answered and their criticisms blunted in advance. Porson I imagine to be a man of taste, but I have my doubts about Aristotle and Samson. Besides, we don't want your time, Winn, to be wasted in explaining the College system, when it could better be used in pointing out to them the special beauties of St. Thomas's."

"Quite right," said Waterlow. "David should start, and I'm not at all sure that he'll find it all that easy to satisfy the quick and carping mind of Aristotle. I'm sure Aristotle felt that David had got away with it when he lectured on the University, and that all sorts of testing questions ought to have been put to him then. He'll be looking for a second chance. Well, so much the better. I like to see a lawyer in difficulties, especially when he meets someone of his own mettle, for without opposition a lawyer is pathetic. Personally, I'd go a little further with our plan. We know that Pacey doesn't believe in the College system, for he told us so. Let us cast him for the part of an American Senator with power to interrupt and object to any part of David's exposition—unless, of course, he feels that he's not a match for counsel on the other side."

"If Prendergast is proposing to do nothing but cry up this ridiculous and wasteful system, I'm only too ready to make my protest at the appropriate moment," answered Pacey rather truculently.

Prendergast laughed. "Of course I'm going to do what I'm

told, and of course I'm going to make a laudation, for I'm briefed, as I understand it, for the College system, and therefore in duty bound to do the best I can for my client. So here goes.

"First of all, then, I will state categorically, in the words of the Handbook to the University, 'for the common purposes of academic life, the Colleges are the University'. (19) Each College is, in fact, a microcosm of the University itself. Freedom and continuity are the hall-marks of the University; freedom and continuity are the hall-marks of the Colleges. A College is autonomous, governed by its own statutes, and responsible to no one but its corporators and its Visitor for its internal administration and policy. Each College has its own Head and Fellows, its own revenues, its own kitchen and Hall and Chapel, its own teaching and bursary staff. It is, in fact, a self-governing community, of which the Head and Fellows form the governing body. Most important of all, a College has an unfettered choice in the selection of its own members—a man may pass Responsions or its equivalent and then become eligible to enter the University, but he cannot actually matriculate until he has found a College to present him. Details vary, but the general picture is the same in the case of each College. There, Robert, how's that for brevity? I opine that I have sketched the picture of the College system in half a dozen bold strokes of the pencil. What will the Senators choose as their point of attack?"

"Aristotle will immediately ask," replied Tennant, "whether this is a truly democratic system or whether a kind of disguised tyranny is exercised by the Heads of Colleges—or he may ask a preliminary question about the constitutional arrangements by which the Head of the Society is chosen."

"In that case I suggest that we relate to them the story of Dr. Jeune," said Gresham. "Dr. Jeune was Master of Pembroke in the middle of the last century; he was also an active member of the Royal Commission on Oxford in 1850; he became Vice-

Chancellor, and later Bishop of Peterborough. In short, he was a distinguished and virtuous man, who rightly, as I suppose, had a proper respect for the dignity of his office and of University institutions (in spite of his reputation as a reformer). One night at a Vice-Cancellarian dinner-party a lady sitting next to him plied him with questions (precisely, my dear Prendergast, as the Senators may ply you). 'Pray, Master,' she said, 'how are Heads of Colleges chosen?' Dr. Jeune, if I may trust to my imagination or my instinct, did not approve of ladies who asked questions; at any rate, he did not give her the sort of answer which our Law Fellow would have drafted. 'Madam,' he said (and again I let my imagination picture his handsome and imposing figure at the head of his own table), 'the Fellows of a College meet together and choose the best-looking among their number to be their Head.' The lady was not satisfied. 'Oh, Master,' she said, 'are you sure that is true? I feel that there must be a mistake somewhere, for I dined with the Provost of Worcester last week.' Dr. Jeune was equal to the occasion. 'Madam,' said he, 'of course I am sure of my facts. You may have dined last week with the Provost, but you have not, I think, met the Fellows of Worcester.'"

"I'm not sure," said Tennant, "that Aristotle will not feel that he is being fobbed off again with an anecdote, and that his desire for accurate information is entirely unsatisfied. And has he not, perhaps, some grounds for suspecting that in certain Colleges the system is not so truly democratic as he could wish? There are all sorts of devious ways through which the Head of a College can exert influence and even, sometimes, have his way against the wishes of most of the Fellows."

"Yes, I have known such instances," admitted Gresham dryly. "When I was on Council one Head of a House was chairman of a committee of which I was a member. We had to discuss a rather controversial matter and make our recommendations. If I remember rightly, there were six of us besides the chairman whom, for the sake of brevity, I shall call the Master, and we found it difficult to come to an agreement. Finally the Master said that, though he regretted the necessity for a vote, there was no other way of reaching a decision. So we voted—six of us for the recommendation and the Master against. I thought that the matter was settled, but I was wrong. 'This is most unfortunate,' said the Master, 'I can only describe the position as a deadlock, and I see no other course open to me but to adjourn the committee for a week.' "

"I hope that you did not give way," said Prendergast, whose sense of legal propriety was touched.

Gresham smiled. "The Master was a very persuasive as well as a determined man. I cannot recall the intervening steps, but I am quite sure that the deadlock, as he called it, was resolved in a manner wholly conformable to his wishes. Yes, I suspect, though I do not know, that in many Colleges the Head of the Society still exercises considerable influence."

"It may be so," said Prendergast, "but I feel compelled to point out that, as your story is concerned with the influence of a Head of a House in a University Committee, it has no relevance whatever to the point at issue. I shall, therefore, maintain for Aristotle's benefit that in the Colleges truly democratic principles prevail. Any invasion of those principles would bring its own well-merited penalty. I once heard a cynic congratulating a newly elected Head of a House. 'You are feeling complacent now,' he said, 'but I must remind you that there is no historical case on record where the Head of a House has not quarrelled with at least a majority of his Fellows within the first two years of his tenure.' If that is not democracy in action, what is? I'm sure that I can convince Aristotle that all the essentials of democratic control are present in the governing body of a College."

"You shock me very much," said Winn, who did not like loose talk about any matter connected with Colleges. "The suggestion that there is not amity and mutual understanding between the Head of a College and the Fellows is repugnant to me, both as a man and as an historian. I'm quite sure that at St. Thomas's such wicked altercations would have been inconceivable. No President of St. Thomas's would have countenanced such things for a moment; Hatfield or Vereker or Eccles or old Fothergill would have been deeply distressed even at the thought of internal divisions of that kind—of course Fothergill was never actually President, though, as I may have told you, he could have been had he wished."

"So much the better for the guide-book," said Prendergast. "We can assert that the College system discourages personal dissension and invite Winn to testify by reference to the history of St. Thomas's. But let me go back now to my main thesis. I've described the system in outline, and I now repeat that the College is a microcosm of the University. To flourish, therefore, it must, above everything else, cherish and maintain its privilege of choosing its own members, resisting all forms of outside interference, and in making that choice it must insist on variety of type. If uniformity and a monotonous mediocrity are fatal to a University, how much more so are they in the smaller and more intimate life of a College? It is harmony that we have to aim at, not uniformity. Of course the scientists present a difficulty. They are, almost of necessity, cut off from the rest in their laboratories, living in a world of their own—but even they must gain something from the fact that we have a residential system. However much they try, they cannot altogether escape from contacts with humane persons, and they must gain some tincture of culture even if they only see their contemporaries in Hall or on the playing fields. Eh, Pacey?"

Tennant hastened to intervene, lest Pacey should take offence. "I think," he said, "that David is trying to provoke you by exaggerated and malicious remarks. Don't let him get away with that. Seriously, though, Senator Pacey, you haven't taken much advantage of your right to interrupt—yet I thought that you were going to traverse all the lawyer's views about the merits of the College system."

Pacey smiled—perhaps a little grimly. "To be quite candid, I thought that the more I interrupted the longer Prendergast would hold forth, and I didn't think that would be for the general good. Besides, I thought that I could put the case on the other side better if I waited till Prendergast had reached the end of his argument. Anyhow, I'll try to tell you now how I look on this particular problem."

Pacey did not find self-expression easy, and he was apt to be left behind in general conversation whilst he was marshalling his ideas. When, however, he spoke on subjects with which he was familiar and about which he had thought, his tone acquired a greater confidence and his voice an unexpected authority.

"I thought," he began, "that I was going to voice the criticisms which many must feel of this much-vaunted College system, but considering the turn which the conversation has taken, I feel impelled first of all to say a word about the position of the scientist. Now I do repudiate as emphatically as I can this belief that scientists are a race apart, segregated from their fellows and only admitted, as it were, by an act of grace to share in the general community of interests which make up a College. The scientist is not the ignorant, one-track-minded creature of your imagination—far from it. I would remind you that no one can come to the University without a qualification in Latin—I don't complain of that, indeed I support it, but I do think that there should be some sort of reciprocity. Can it be right that in the modern world any so-called educated person should be wholly without even an elementary knowledge of natural science? We scientists may not fully understand or appreciate you old-fashioned scholars, but do you even begin to understand us?

Think again of this supposed narrowness of the scientific mind. What could be further from the truth? I suppose that you would agree, you historians, that scientific method dates from the Renaissance, for it's the spirit of enquiry and criticism which supplants the old blind acceptance of authority. That's what I mean by the scientific approach. We proceed patiently from the known to the unknown, each advance leading to the next; we will not accept anything unless we can verify it by experiment; nor reject anything just because we are told that we should. Think of Leonardo, Mitton, and compare him with your Churchmen of the time (no, don't interrupt me, or I shall lose the thread). Where is the narrowness in his case? Was there ever a man of more universal interests? And think of the problems of flight. '*Mitton, hadst thou been living at that hour*', you would have said (forgive my grammar, Gresham) that God had ordained that fishes should swim in the sea, and birds should fly in the air and men should walk on the earth; how impious to suggest that men might fly! Not so Leonardo! He makes drawing after drawing of the wings of birds, he studies the mathematics of flight and experiments in every direction. Which has the narrow mind—Mitton or Leonardo? There can be only one answer. Isn't it true that authoritarians would, if they could, have kept the world in a fixed unchanging form—and that order and not progress was their goal? From that, as I believe, they were rescued by the scientists, or at least by those who had the scientific mind. And so it must always be. Go into the College Library and you will find that Winn and Gresham and all of you place the greatest value on the oldest, and most useless, books. Go into a library of science and you will find that the newest book, if it is sound, supersedes the older books on the same subject and makes them worthless. You live in the past, but we live in the future. If, then, the pursuit of truth is the function of a University, how can any but the scientists hold the most honoured place? How can you know, as we do, the burning enthusiasm which comes from discovery? How can you enjoy that highest of all pleasures—the feeling of having added something, however small, to the sum of human knowledge, of having assisted, if only by a little, in the progress of humanity?"

He checked himself and smiled. "So you see I'm entirely of one mind with you that a College should aim at variety of type among its members, though no doubt I should mix the ingredients in different proportions to yours. But I do beg you to clear your minds of that delusion that we scientists are a small, narrow-minded set of pariahs among you. Concentrate rather on the universality of the Renaissance mind."

Pacey paused as though expecting objections, but no one seemed anxious to accept the implied challenge. So he continued:

"I ought to be talking about the College system and the collection of all types of men within the walls of a residential College. I hope you see now that it's not as a scientist that I oppose the system, for indeed it seems to me axiomatic that if Colleges exist in their present form they should contain representatives of all kinds of studies and interests. No, I only criticise our present arrangement as a practical man. I'm profoundly convinced, as most of you are, that men come to a University primarily to acquire knowledge—to seek it out for themselves, not to have it rammed down their throats. They will go where the great teachers and researchers are, and those should go who are best qualified to make use of their opportunities. For that reason I advocate a straightforward competitive examination for admission to the whole University.

"When you have collected the men, what do you gain by this artificial division of them into Colleges? I agree up to a point in the advantages of a residential University, but surely you should centre teaching and administration in the University and not scatter your control among twenty-five Colleges. If five or six thousand young men are concentrated in one University city, they will have no difficulty in joining together in clubs and societies or in creating the organisations they need for sport or relaxation, whether they're in College or not. Have you not observed in a foreign hotel how two bridge players will attract others of like taste as readily as a magnet draws iron? What is the need for your elaborate College system? And consider the disadvantages! Take management to begin with. I don't remember exactly how many Colleges there are—twenty-two or twenty-three, or twenty-four, it makes little difference—but I know that each of them has, for example, its own Head and Bursar and kitchen. I've never studied catering scientifically, and I don't know what the best economic unit for feeding a community is, but I should guess that a thousand, say, or at any rate six or seven hundred, is a more economic total than two hundred and fifty. Why should not St. Thomas's and some other great College share a common kitchen, or why should not Exeter and Jesus and Lincoln combine for a common kitchen and common meals? Trower could give us some idea of the waste that would be prevented by some such efficient system and the financial saving in staff alone that would result. Or consider our estates and the estates of other Colleges. How many College estates could be controlled by one really competent estates Bursar acting not for one but, say, three or four Colleges? How many acres scattered over how many counties could he properly attend to? I do not know, but I do know that the present system is ludicrously wasteful and inefficient. I've studied the history of our College in an amateur way, and I think I've some idea of what St. Thomas's was like in the reign of Queen Victoria. What should we not have gained if the management of our estates had been taken out of the fumbling hands of a moribund clergyman and placed in the secure grasp of a trained and qualified estate agent, even if we had had to suffer the ignominy of sharing our agent with Oriel or Trinity or Jesus? I assert nothing, I only ask. And then consider teaching. Isn't it a matter of simple social justice that a student, if worthy, should have the best instruction that the University can provide? Why should a man be condemned to inferior teaching because he happens by chance to have gone to a College where his own particular subject is less well taught than at other Colleges? But I'm less concerned with that aspect of the problem because science will force reform on you there whether you like it or not. The laboratory is and must be independent of Colleges and artificial distinctions of that kind. Then research. Posts are offered haphazard by Colleges; they ought to be offered by the University and in subjects where research can most profitably be applied. But I must not go on too long. Really all this is not disloyalty to the College, it's just plain common sense. The College system has grown up as a product of the past, and no one ever troubles to consider if it is suitable in modern conditions. So I say, scrap it! Let the University take over the whole academic control, let the Colleges pool their resources, and let them remain, if at all, as residential hostels and social centres. All that the College system has done is to create an artificial standard of living, and make it impossible for any except the well-to-do to come here at all. The expense of a University education has prevented countless numbers of students from ever being educated at all. I admit that the Socialist State has rectified that, but it cannot correct all the blunders of the past. Why should not students flock here to study as they did in the Middle Ages and make their own arrangements for their board and lodging and their social life? If we are honest, must we not admit that the College system has restricted University life to a privileged class and confined learning to the rich?"

He stopped abruptly and there was a rather uneasy silence.

"Really, Pacey," said Winn at length, "all this is quite shocking."

"It was meant to be," said Pacey.

Winn had not really grasped the greater part of the argument, but he realised that his most cherished beliefs had been attacked and that some protest was necessary.

"I have never heard it even suggested that our chef was inferior to those of the other Colleges you mentioned," he remarked. "So your plan for bolshevising our kitchen (if you will forgive the phrase) seems to me absurd."

Tennant, however, was disposed to treat the matter more seriously. "I am afraid," he said, "that, as editor of the guidebook, I have neglected Dr. Johnson's wise advice never to let the Whig dogs have the best of it. Really, Pacey, you have made out a strong case."

"Yes," added Waterlow with an acid smile. "Mitton, I fancy, was about to remark '*And even the ranks of Tuscany could scarce forbear to cheer*'."

Mitton bit his lip, for he had in fact been prevented from quoting the line only by his uncertainty whether the second word was 'even' or 'e'en'.

Gresham, however, came to the rescue of the others, and took up the cudgels on the other side.

"I agree, Pacey," he began, "that you have a case, and that you have put it fairly and moderately—yet in my bones I feel that you are wrong. Let me say a word first about the subject of the scientist. To me it seems that the fact—for it is a fact—that the scientists are to some extent separated from the rest of us suggests not that the College system should be scrapped, but that College attachments should be strengthened. I'm willing to admit that we humanists have more to learn from the scientists than they from us, but I'm sure that closer union would be advantageous to both. The pursuit of truth in itself cannot produce evil, but the application of scientific knowledge can. I am one of those who think that scientific advance has been more speedy than the

233

advance in, say, moral philosophy, and that the first needs the brake which can be applied by the second. The instrument of scientific knowledge is immensely, terrifyingly powerful; it is for us all to see to it that it is used and applied wisely and beneficently. Don't let us quarrel about the degree of responsibility which each of us carries. It might well be argued that the gifts of science were being used for purposes of destruction, but it could equally be maintained that destructive weapons were less harmful to the human race than, let us say, lying propaganda. It seems to me, then, that closer liaison and more intimate collaboration are needed between the two parties. I have to admit that in some Common Rooms scientists, who are to some extent newcomers, do feel a little alien in a society of predominantly humane scholars. I regret this, but surely the remedy is not that which Pacey proposes.

"That brings me to the College system, and all my training and all my instincts lead me to defend that. Does not each one of us who has been educated here *know* that he has derived untold benefit from attachment to a College? But why? I wonder myself if it is not, perhaps, in the last analysis a matter of size. When Mazzini was defending the theory of nationality he did so on the ground that humanity was something too great for the individual to comprehend. 'The individual is too weak and humanity is too vast. My God, prays the Breton mariner as he puts out to sea, protect me, my ship is so little, and Thy Ocean so great!' The cosmopolitan who talks of humanity and neglects the nation is as one who bids men climb a ladder and takes away the rungs. I cannot help thinking that something of the same sort is true of the University and the Colleges. For loyalty to be strong it must be limited. Personally I've never ceased to be grateful to Providence for so ordering my life that I belong to a profession in which I am a member of a society, small enough to be intimate, large enough to give me all the interests I need. I should suppose that the member of a large family, or a clan, might have this too, but not, I think, one of a small family. What pleasure is really comparable to that of sharing and rejoicing in the successes of one's friends? Everyone enjoys vicarious pleasure of that kind. See how a schoolboy attaches himself with feverish enthusiasm to the fortunes of this first-class county cricket side or that leading football club! Besides, loyalty depends not only on the benefits one receives but also on the contributions which one makes. Admit, Pacey, for you are an honest man, that you have derived more genuine satisfaction from what you have given to societies to which you have belonged than from what you have received from them.

"I think, too, that you underestimate the practical advantages of the College—and also of the tutorial—system. Of course your point about social justice and the best teacher is a sound one, but isn't it also a little doctrinaire? If one teacher is outstanding isn't it a sheer impossibility that all those who wish to learn directly from him should, in fact, be able to do so? And there are great advantages on the other side, notably the personal interest of the College tutor. The College tutor may indeed not have the expert knowledge of the professor—he may even lack the gift of exposition, but he does know the pupils' private interests and weaknesses, and he does know when the pupil should be encouraged or stimulated or reproved. I cannot but think that the personal relation—the human touch, if you prefer the phrase—is of greater importance than the eminence of the professor. (20) Even if a man has to be 'farmed out', as the phrase goes, to some tutor in another College he can feel confident that someone in his own College is watching his interests. Nor can I accept the argument that the College system has excluded all but the richer students from the University. It has perhaps raised the standard of undergraduate life, but should we not applaud rather than condemn that tendency?

"I agree wholeheartedly with David's remark that the un-fettered right of the College to choose its own members—senior as well as junior—is a priceless boon, for each College has its own ethos and its own requirements, and those it must maintain. In these days of Government grants the University may find itself, sooner or later, compelled to admit some and reject others at the behest of an outside authority. Should that happen, the Colleges remain the only effective defence for academic freedom. Well, that's my case. It's not well argued, I fear, perhaps because it's a creed of the heart rather than of the head—but I'm profoundly convinced that for good or ill the College system is the essence of Oxford life, and that, if you believe in Oxford, you must accept the College system."

"When I undertook to defend the College system," said Prendergast dryly, "I imagined that my brief would be marked with a substantial refresher, but I am beginning to think that my learned junior has robbed me of my thunder. Seriously, aren't we making too much of all this? I know it's a question which could be debated almost indefinitely, but our prime object is to explain Oxford to the Senators, and I really doubt whether they will stand for such a long and theoretical discussion."

"I'm bound to say that I agree with you," Tennant replied. "I always felt that this was the most critical controversy which would emerge in the course of our discussions; but I do not think that we ought to expose our differences too openly to the Senators. If ever I write my longer work, my great book on Oxford, I promise you that I'll do justice to both sides in the controversy, but for the present guide-book I feel inclined to skate quickly over the thin ice. Could we not tell the Senators that the College system is almost universally regarded as the most characteristic feature—or peculiarity—of Oxford life, and go on to describe the different Colleges? I'm sorry, though, that we cannot show a united front."

To everyone's surprise, one of his rare smiles lit up Pacey's usually rather stern face.

"You know," he said, "Gresham's remark about the head and the heart came home to me, too. My mind tells me that the College system is in theory wasteful and wrong, but none the less, even in the short time I've been here, I've felt a growing sentimental attachment and loyalty to St. Thomas's. I'm quite ready to dig my toes in and argue with any of you here, but somehow (I'm almost ashamed to admit) I couldn't help rallying to your support if we have a dispute with the Senators. For my part, I'm ready to close the ranks. If you try to interfere with a man who is beating his wife, you know, they are both apt to turn on you together. So you may count in the wicked and ignorant scientist as a College, and particularly a St. Thomas's, fan for this occasion only."

"Really," murmured Winn to himself, "I believe that Pacey is quite a nice-minded young man, after all."

Tennant was openly relieved. "I'm glad about that," he said, "for now in the guide-book we can discuss the Colleges as we know them, without arguing about the justification for the system itself. I rather fancy that they will be specially interested in the differences between Colleges. Aristotle, we agreed, is sure to be a bachelor, but Porson and Samson will be considering sending their sons to Oxford, and they'll want to know how to choose a College. Why, in your opinion, Winn, is St. Thomas's the best College in the University? Do we provide better teaching, have we sounder institutions or more effective financial control, or better rooms and buildings than the rest?"

Winn replied without any of his usual hesitation. "None of those things matter at all. It's men and not institutions that are of importance. If good men come to a College, a College is always good. You need pursue the matter no further."

"That is all very well," said Tennant, "but I don't think that the problem is quite so easy as that. What do you mean by 'good men' in the first place, and why do 'good men' come to St. Thomas's in the second?"

"I am tempted to interject at this point," remarked Gresham, "that Aristotle (the original Aristotle, I mean, not our American friend) maintains convincingly that the qualities of the good man and the good citizen are not identical. Isn't the same true when we consider the good man and the good member of a College?"

"Precisely," agreed Tennant. "But I'm not sure that we ought not to consider an even more fundamental question first. Quite apart from selecting a College, why do men want to come to Oxford at all?"

"I should say," said Prendergast, "that in the past most men came for one of two reasons. I believe that the number who came for sheer love of learning was, *pace* Gresham, negligible. They came either because a degree was a necessary qualification for a career in the Church or in the learned professions, or because they wished to pass three or four years in congenial surroundings and because there was a social convention that that was the right thing to do. Nowadays the great majority come because they believe (I hope rightly) that an Oxford education will be of service to them in their careers and will enable them to obtain lucrative employment. You will call me a cynic, but I think that my analysis is in the main true."

"That you greatly underestimate the number of those who come under the influence of higher motives, I am quite sure," answered Gresham, "and I'm still more certain that you do not appreciate the spell which the love of learning casts on many men. Still, I will admit that this belief in the desirability of an Oxford education has fundamentally changed our problem. In the old days (the good old days, as I think) you could, provided that you reached a not very lofty intellectual standard, just come to the University. You arrived, so to speak, and hung up your hat in the hall. Let me quote to you some remarks from the reminiscences of an old College butler, who started his career, it seems, in 1881, for it gives a vivid picture of the manner in which a College was made up in those days.

" 'My duty in Hall as a junior servant was to wait on the Freshmen. If we got 17 or 18 in October it was thought the College had done well. There were always a few who had been turned down by some other College, but most of them declared they were glad they had come to us. [There's the College spirit working, Pacey.] They were admitted to College by a short entrance examination. I don't remember anyone failing in this, even if they had to be sent down later on. They saw Oxford life as it was then, made many friends, learnt how to carry their wine, how to carve, and meet other men's sisters and many engagements began in this way.'

"I like that picture of an older Oxford, and for our purposes it indicates the great change which has occurred. It was easy, if you could afford it, to come to Oxford then; nowadays the applicant for a place in a College can be compared—not inaptly—to the camel trying to make his way through the needle's eye. There's a good and a bad side to that. Sometimes I think that the reform which has made it possible for everyone who is fitted for a University education to have it is the greatest social advance made in our lifetime. Sometimes, however, I have my uneasy doubts. I'm not sure that those who really desired to come in the past were often excluded—a way used to be found, even if it was a hard way. There's something to be said for making achievement difficult, and we all know the triumphs of the poor scholar with his sack of oatmeal. Besides, it seems to me wholly commendable that those who have saved money should wish to spend it on their children's education—to give their children the best that they can. Perhaps that meant that a good many young men came to the University who were not obviously fitted for the academic life, but are we not threatened nowadays with the opposite danger? I mean that we only fill the University with scholars and near-scholars and exclude all others. I seem to see a horrifying picture of monotonous mediocrity. I know that you will think that I'm illogical, for I've always said that those should come here who love the things of the mind and who wish to follow the paths of learning, but then I can't persuade myself that such folk are only to be found among the scholar class. I'm just thinking aloud and you must pardon my rambling remarks."

Tennant laughed. "But, my dear Gresham, surely no apology is called for. I, for my part, agree with almost all that you have said. I'm sure that the great change which has occurred is just that which you have described. Formerly anyone could come here, and the undergraduate chose his College at will; nowadays the College chooses its undergraduates from among a crowd of eager applicants. The problem is to choose wisely. If we accept everyone and go back to Pacey's medieval University with its tens of thousands of students, we shall spoil the life here for all; if we exclude some we must take care that we do not exclude men who would be of value to our community. Do you know Swift's lines?

> We are the chosen few,
> All others will be damned.
> There is no room in Heaven for you,
> We can't have Heaven crammed.

That's the College problem to-day, but it also suggests the right solution. As I see it, in the past each College built up some sort of special character for itself—or perhaps that character just grew. Gresham would say that each College had and has its own ethos. Even we, who know something of modern changes, think instinctively of the popular conceptions of our youth when we think of individual Colleges. We think of the regal splendour of Christ Church, of the catholicity of type in Balliol and of its scholarship strengthened and fortified by its Scottish infiltration; we think of the tough North Country basis of Queen's, or the solid virtue of New College, or the athletic vigour and corporate spirit of Brasenose."

"I cannot agree," said Waterlow. "Surely each individual thinks of different things when he enters a College. To me Brasenose immediately calls up visions of Walter Pater (but then, as you know, I'm not really interested in athletics); I never enter Trinity without thinking of dining clubs—simply because it chanced that the first dining club I ever attended was in that College; Exeter for me is Lorna Doone and all the magic of the West Country; and Pembroke immediately recalls to me 'Charley's Aunt', for, so I have been told, the quadrangle there was the scene of that immortal party. Anyhow, I will not agree for a moment that all of us have the same impression of each individual College, and, as I said before, reputation lags its full generation behind the truth. And as for Univ.," he added as an afterthought, "it would be impossible for me to pass its gates without thinking of the bust of King Alfred, which used to stand on the mantelpiece in the Senior Common Room—proudly declaring that fable was mightier than truth. I trust, Robert, that the guide-book will be firm in attributing the foundation of Univ. to King Alfred."

"I'm sorry," Tennant laughed, "but I doubt whether even guide-book truth could be stretched so far."

"Do you think," asked Mitton, "that the differences between Colleges have disappeared with the new dispensation?"

"Certainly not," Tennant answered, "and I should fight to the last ditch to maintain the better features of individual Colleges. It's just in that way that the College system can be useful in maintaining freedom of opinion and variety in the University—

for I too, like Gresham, see the danger of a University submerged under a wave of monotonous mediocrity. No, the choice of men for a College has become far more important than ever before, and only, as Winn said, by a wise selection can the reputation of a College—St. Thomas's or any other—be maintained or enhanced."

"And what will you tell the Senators," asked Pacey, "about your methods of selection, should they chance to ask you how angels are selected for entry into your St. Thomas's heaven? You've been concerned a good deal with admissions here since the war, haven't you?"

Tennant laughed. "It won't be just a competitive examination, Pacey," he replied, "there is more to it than that. But I mustn't refuse your challenge, and I'll try to tell the Senators something at least of our methods.

"To begin with there must be room for anyone who has a real intellectual spark—for anyone who is clearly and indubitably above the ordinary level of his competitors. He may get a scholarship or he may not; if the promise or possibility of intellectual distinction is there, it is enough. The men that I am suspicious of are those who have by intensive teaching and even by great personal effort been brought into the 'near-scholar' class so far as examinations are concerned. Too often they are men who can never expect to go further, and who would gain as much or as little, if they continued their studies in Oxford or in any other place. Well, the choice of intellectuals is easy— difficulties begin when you have to fill up the list of commoners. Of course everyone who is to be considered must pass the College entrance examination—that is a qualifying test, designed to make it clear that everyone who is accepted is at least capable of proceeding eventually to a degree. But then there is not room for nearly all those who pass, or could pass, that test. It is when we are trying to select from among those who are qualified for acceptance that we must take other considerations to mind; it's then I think that we are entitled, and right, to give weight to other qualifications besides, say, Latin prose or elementary mathematics."

"What other considerations would come in?" asked Pacey. "What would help a man to gain admittance here if his intellectual standard was adequate but not more? What qualities would you take into account, what would you put to his credit?"

"Perhaps others of you could help me to answer that question," said Tennant, looking towards Winn.

"Connection with the College," said Winn. "That should be the first consideration. A man whose father or grandfather or brother or uncle has been in the College should have the first claim. Men who have a family connection seem to understand the College from the moment that they arrive, and they always want to come here. That's very important, I'm sure. I remember that we very nearly ploughed a young man many years ago because he knew hardly anything, and we had not realised that he was a great-nephew of old Fothergill's. Dear me, we might have committed a great act of injustice."

Tennant nodded. "I agree that family connections should be encouraged, and still more that a real enthusiasm to come here should be taken into account; but there are many other factors."

"Granted that the present system is accepted," said Pacey, "I feel very strongly that room should be found for a reasonably large number of scientists—indeed, on your own showing, they cannot be excluded—and they might in time raise the whole standard of the place."

"You must not forget," Mitton hastily interposed, "that the College is a place of religion as well as of education. For the good of all, as well as for their own benefit, you ought, I am sure, to keep up the number of ordinands."

"You are both right in a way," said Prendergast, "but not,

I think, for precisely the right reasons. Is not the great merit of the College system that it provides tutorial instruction for men within the College? That being so, the first need is to arrange that the men are conveniently disposed among the different subjects. I submit that a College entirely composed of scientists or of ordinands—or of lawyers for that matter—would be intolerable, but, further, that even a disproportion between the subjects would be inconvenient if it meant that one tutor was hopelessly overloaded and another comparatively idle. Other things being equal, the commoners' places should be rationed out among the different faculties according to our tutorial strength."

Trower had taken little interest in the evening's discussion, but he now entered the debate. "I know you think me an out-of-date Philistine," he began in a not very ingratiating tone, "but I feel it necessary to say something now in the name of ordinary horse-sense. It's damned silly to pretend that a College can flourish and gain a name in the world if it neglects sport and athletics. I'm all for seeing St. Thomas's men taking their firsts in schools—what do we elect the scholars for, anyhow?—but I'm certain sure that anyone who gains athletic distinction adds to the reputation of the College, and often adds to it more than a successful scholar can. To my mind anyone who shows ability in any sphere is doing a service to the society to which he belongs. For God's sake, don't argue yourselves into the position where you want to exclude from St. Thomas's the ordinary, straightforward, healthy, old-fashioned, out-of-door type of undergraduate. He's always been the backbone of the place, and he always will be."

"May I put in a plea for other depressed classes?" asked Waterlow. "I agree with Trower that the athlete should still have his place, but I should like to think that there was room still for the old-fashioned pass-man. Surely he has a claim? It's true

UNDERGRADUATE CONVERSATION PIECE, from the painting by Edward I. Halliday

that he could not rise to the intellectual level of his honours brother, but I'm sure that in many cases he gained more from Oxford and valued his gains more than most men do. We talk of equality of opportunity. Should we not give opportunity to those who start with a handicap but who may hope to improve?"

"Your argument to me," objected Pacey, "sounds very much like a request that the College should admit all who do worst in the entrance examination."

"No, no," said Waterlow. "I'm only pleading for a small leaven of pass-men in our learned lump. It's hard to select them, I know, but I believe the effort worth making. Still I won't press that point, because I have another to make, to which I attach much greater importance. I hope, yes I hope fervently, that the College will always find room for some at least who come here primarily to enjoy themselves. We talk so much of Oxford being a place where men can learn things in other ways than from books, and where they can make friendships and learn the art of living. I know that we cannot revive the carefree existence of forty years back, but it cannot be wrong—it simply cannot be wrong—that the young should have some happy years, some time not wholly overshadowed by responsibilities and hard economic realities. I've often criticised my own countrymen because they seem to resent each other's enjoyment of life. If you feel gay and fortunate and anxious to celebrate your feelings of satisfaction in France or Italy, every stranger seems to be on your side; in England I have often in similar circumstances been sensible of an atmosphere of almost resentful criticism. For heaven's sake, let those be happy who can! Sorrow and difficulty, you know, are supposed to strengthen human nature, but happiness enriches it. Besides, success—whether in the schools or the playing fields or in society or in clubs—is good, and not bad, for the great majority of men. It improves them; it makes them more charitable to their fellows. Human beings fulfil and express themselves in many different ways, and he would be a bold man who would maintain that only those who follow the orthodox path can travel with advantage along life's road. Didn't we notice when we were talking about eighteenth-century Oxford that some of the best products of the human mind were the outcome of chance and freedom and variety rather than of uniform organization? I'd go further than that. Long ago when I was reading my Italian poets I came across Giusti's 'Memorie di Pisa', in which he describes his own feelings when his University career was over. No one, I think, could have been an idler student than Giusti; yet how much he profited from his University life! And how well he states the case for those of his kidney—how well he shows that they, as well as the grim and unresponsive scholars, have their place in our society:

> A quelli il popolo,
> Che teme un morso,
> Fa largo, e subito
> Muta discorso:
> A noi repubblica
> Di lieto umore,
> Tutti spalancano
> Le braccia e il core:
> A conti fatti,
> Beati i matti!

So, I say, let us find room for some of those who come here for the enjoyment of life, even if they be idlers or dilettanti, for they will, I do assure you, add to the happiness of others besides themselves."

Gresham had followed Waterlow's argument with the keenest attention, and now began to explain his own point of view.

"I've a great deal of sympathy with Waterlow's plea," he said, "especially because those whom he champions would bring variety into our society. Casting my mind back to my own under-graduate days, I recall very clearly that I owed as much to an American Rhodes Scholar as to any other of my contemporaries. It was not that he was a specially clever man or a particularly learned one, but he had experience of life and manners beyond the ken of a shy British freshman, and he opened many doors for me into new and fascinating worlds. That's why I should always press for the entry here of a number of men from overseas—from America and from the Orient too—for I'm sure that they would contribute as much as they could hope themselves to acquire from Oxford. Then, too, I'm impressed by the thought that opportunity should be given to all who can hope to use it. I've always thought that Aristotle (my Greek Aristotle; how I wish that this American gentleman had not been given a name which leads to so much confusion!) stated a profound truth when he said that a man possessing one virtue was eventually capable of all. That is why, in my opinion, we should also seek to find out if candidates have some special interest or private hobby of their own, in which they have shown promise or even performance. No matter what it is! I'm disposed to think well of a man who, for example, plays the flute better than anyone else in Wiltshire, because I feel that he will be able to contribute something to the general good and because I think that he is likely to develop in other ways."

Pacey's mind worked a little slowly, but it was sure.

"But," he said, "the man whom you reject—I mean the man who fails to get a scholarship and is condemned always to be a 'failed-scholar'—has at least shown the virtue of industry; why should not he acquire the other virtues?"

"I was thinking," Gresham replied, "rather of virtues outside the normal curriculum. What is needed, I think, is some interest which has grown up of itself, and which has not been forced or imposed. There was a story current in my day of a freshman scholar at Balliol. One man and one party after another visited him in his rooms. Would he play Rugby football? No. Would he join the Union? No. Or the Labour and Liberal and Conservative Clubs? No. Or come down to the river and row? No. And at last he overcame his shyness sufficiently to burst out with a disclaimer. 'It's no good, gentlemen, I'm just Mathematics.' "

"And did he so remain?" asked Prendergast.

"No. That's the satisfactory part of the story. Someone, more perceptive than the rest, discovered that he had a secret passion for sailing and for the sea. They went to sail a boat on the Upper River, and then they went to sail together on the sea. All that opened a new world to him. From sailing he moved on to the problems of flight, and from those problems to flying itself—and well, I needn't carry the story further."

"It's really a matter for congratulation," said Tennant, cordially but a little pompously, "that on this our last night everyone has shown such an admirable team spirit. I think that everyone has helped over this question of admissions, and it only remains for me to pull the whole together. As editor of the guide-book, I feel myself in agreement with all the contributors to a greater or less degree. But I don't think that some of you have made the most of your arguments. Take, for instance, the athletes and Waterlow's idlers; it's not only a question of what they gain, but what other people gain from them. I can't deny myself the pleasure of quoting to you part of a letter which I read in *The Times* only a short time ago. It is written by a learned man to protest against the proposal that Universities should be filled entirely by scholarship winners, or in other words that places should be allotted according to an order of merit made out after competitive examination:

"...The proposal", as Aristotle said of a somewhat similar proposal of Plato, "appears to wear an attractive face and to argue benevolence: the hearer receives it gladly." But does it, as Aristotle went on to ask, really square with human nature and life? Does it wash? I was admitted to a University myself, nearly sixty years ago, on a test of merit. There were others like me. But there were also others of a different sort who came because their fathers and their fathers' fathers had come, and because their fathers could pay. It did me a world of good to mix with men of this latter sort. I learned that intellectuals, by themselves, make a bleak sort of society. I learned that a University is, and should be, a meeting-ground of all sorts and conditions of men: both rich and poor, both men from homes of old culture and manners and men who have to start from scratch in making their own culture and manners. I learned that if you make intellectuals, as defined by marks in an order of merit, the whole of a University society, you do irreparable damage to your intellectuals. You deprive them of the benefits of cross-fertilisation from other types of mind and character, which may in their way be equally valuable to the world, and are, anyhow, necessary to that process of student inter-education which is one of the greatest gains of University life. I suppose I am an intellectual myself. Deliver me, I pray, from the sole society of my kind: it takes all sorts to make a world—even the little world of the University.' (21)

"I doubt if the point could be better put. To me it seems beyond dispute that a College must aim at variety of type and variety of interests among its members. And the College, nowadays, rather than the University, is the guardian of the gate, who bids one enter and another stay outside. If anything decides the standing and reputation of a College, it is surely the selection of its members."

"I'm not disputing your judgment," said Pacey, "but one thing puzzles me. Everyone here (even myself, though grudgingly) admits that Colleges differ from one another and that some are at one time better (though that's a vague term) and at other times worse than others. Further, everyone agrees that St. Thomas's is incomparably the best and the most favoured of Colleges, yet very few of us were undergraduates here. How did we, or the majority of us, transfer our loyalty so wholeheartedly? Doesn't it suggest that this College loyalty is somewhat artificial?"

Tennant shook his head. "No, I don't think so. It's rare to find that a man cannot take his place in a society to which he moves. I heard not long ago a wise and thoughtful man speaking on this very point. He had been recently appointed to an important post, which necessitated a change of Colleges, and what he said was this: 'I do not find that my loyalties are divided, but rather they have been multiplied.' But loyalty is a big subject, and it's past midnight. If we are going to be at out best for the Senators to-morrow we ought to be making for our beds."

CHAPTER IX

Tennant was early abroad on the Wednesday morning—early, that is, by his own vacation standards. It was hardly ten o'clock when he was already in confabulation with the chef, to whom he gave his last instructions with regard to the luncheon and dinner which he had ordered some days previously; twenty minutes later he was in close parley with Callender, the College Butler—the only human being whose judgment of wine he ranked almost as high as his own; from the butler he passed on to the Head Porter.

"Martin," he said, "I am expecting three gentlemen from America between eleven-thirty and twelve. As soon as they arrive I want them shown up to my rooms."

Duty thus satisfied, Tennant retired to his rooms, where he had instructed all his collaborators to meet him at eleven for a glass of sherry before the day's work began.

When the whole party was assembled, Tennant gave to each a small bundle of type-written notes. "I've made the notes short," he said, "because really they are only your cues. You all know your stuff so well that it's not necessary to put it all on paper, but these notes will remind you of the topics we decided to discuss with reference to the sights which we show the Senators. And I've put down the names of those who have volunteered to do any special piece of exposition. I'm having a much longer booklet prepared which will include the substance of what each of us says, and will be, in fact, the famous guide-book. It isn't quite ready yet, but I've no doubt that it will be completed in time for me to give the Senators each a copy before they leave."

He looked round the room with evident satisfaction.

"Really, you know," he went on, "I must congratulate you all on your work. I've no doubt that Boomer, with his odious taste for jokes, thought that his senatorial friends would ask us all sorts of questions which we couldn't answer. However, I don't think that we can credit the great Sir John with sufficient brains to embarrass the Fellows of St. Thomas's. It's really rather clumsy of him to think that we should not be able to see through his little plot and take steps to frustrate it. Anyhow, we have our guide-book ready, and armed with it we can answer any question which is put to us."

"Aren't you being a little hubristic?" asked Waterlow. "We've not seen the Senators yet, and they may be more learned and more curious than you suppose."

"We have no evidence that they are even Senators," added Pacey. "They might possibly be experts in higher education or professors of architecture or specialists of that kind."

"Nonsense," answered Tennant. "Boomer's friends *must* be Senators; we had that all out days ago. And of course there is no question which such men can ask which we, as a team, fortified by the guide-book, cannot answer. After all our labours, we are entitled to feel confident. But I'll give you a toast. 'Success to the guide-book, and may the Senators ask no question to which it cannot provide an answer.' "

At that moment came a knock at the door, accompanied by the rasping cough with which Martin was accustomed to announce his presence. "Mr. Tennant, Sir," he said in tones in which respect and reproof were nicely blended, "three American young ladies to see you, Sir."

The glasses which had been lifted for the toast were held in mid-air as though the group of men had been frozen suddenly into immobility—and the three young ladies stepped into the room. In their sudden embarrassment no one of the men present could have given a clear description of the unexpected visitors;

it was only later, when impressions could be compared, that a clear picture of the three could be drawn. Trower, who prided himself on being a misogynist, spoke disrespectfully of "those school-girls" and Winn asserted (though no one believed him) that he could not distinguish between "those three charming American ladies". In fact, they bore little resemblance to each other. The first was small, but vivacious and attractive, and no one who even glanced at her could doubt that she was the possessor of both intelligence and taste. (What is the feminine of Porson, murmured Waterlow to himself.) The second was also good-looking—or would have been if her appearance had not been to some extent spoiled by horn-rimmed spectacles and a look of almost oppressively earnest intelligence. (I suppose a girl *could* be called Aristotle, whispered Waterlow.) No one could have described the third member of the party as merely attractive or even good-looking—she was beautiful. Critics might, indeed, have suggested that she was a little lacking in animation and per-haps that intellectually she might fall behind her companions, but her beauty alone was enough. Every male eye in the room followed her instinctively. (Delilah, without a doubt, said Water-low.) Perhaps her face would not have launched a thousand ships, but it was well capable of capsizing the not very seaworthy aca-demic hearts of some of the members of the St. Thomas's Senior Common Room.

Tennant, whose unintentional ejaculation "My God" was sufficiently a whisper to be heard by all, made the first effort to pull himself together.

"I'm delighted to see you," he said, "you must be——"

"Oh, Mr. Tennant," said the first, "how varry, varry stupid of me. Why of course you don't even know our names. I'm Betty Perkins [Why couldn't it have been Porson, thought Waterlow], and this is Janet Anderson, and this is Virginia Sturges ["Whom I shall always call Delilah," whispered Waterlow to Prendergast].

We were simply thrilled when Sir John told us that you would show us all over Oxford. He said there wasn't a soul that could do it as well as you, unless Mr. Winn was here. Why, you must be Mr. Winn, I'm sure you are from Sir John's description. Well, we are just pleased to meet you. It's too good of you to look after us like this."

She flashed a dazzling smile on Tennant and Winn, whilst Virginia smiled with even more effect on Mitton and Pacey, who were, as she had quickly perceived, a little younger than the rest of the company. Trower instinctively fingered his short but trim moustache.

With less than his usual aplomb, Tennant made the necessary introductions. "And everyone here," he added, with a smile which failed to carry conviction and did not seem to be infectious, "is keenly looking forward to showing you all our local sights and telling you our traditional stories."

"Yes, indeed," said Waterlow, who had no intention of allowing Tennant to escape from his responsibilities. "Why, Tennant has actually written a special guide-book to Oxford in your honour."

"That's the greatest compliment I've ever had," Betty said with enthusiasm. "It'll make the visit perfect. We can see all the sights by day and read our guide-book in the evening."

"I'm afraid," said Tennant, "that the book isn't quite ready yet, though I hope it will be before you leave—and it may be rather dull reading for you."

"Dull, oh no! I'm sure it will be thrilling. It will tell us every single thing."

"Not that," protested Tennant, "though I hope it may give you some idea of Oxford—that is, of course, if I can get it finished in time. [Which God forbid", he added under his breath.] "Anyhow, I think we ought to regard it as a last resource, to be referred to only if we cannot answer your questions ourselves."

Prendergast came, rather maladroitly, to his assistance.

"Yes, I see it like this. Everyone is asking questions and trying to settle some impossibly difficult conundrum and then from under his coat Mr. Punch produces his two hundredth volume and hands it to them with courtly grace. Then of course everything is cleared up and settled at once."

"But who is Mr. Punch?" asked Virginia in a voice so rich and pleasing that Mitton found himself wishing that he was the subject of her question.

"Why, honey, of course the guide-book will tell you that," said Betty, with a dangerously intelligent twinkle in her eye.

"Not exactly," said Tennant. "The guide-book confines itself to purely Oxford matters. *Punch*, you know, is an English repository of humour—a great national possession. I suppose that it would correspond to your *New Yorker*, which an American Rhodes Scholar sends us for the Common Room. Of course our idea of humour is not quite the same as yours; perhaps we can fairly claim a rather wider—or should I say deeper—sense of appreciation. Still every now and then the *New Yorker* does strike a rich vein of humour which we can all equally enjoy. I remember a picture—a quite admirable picture—of a large, pompous, imposing parson preaching from a pulpit; you could feel that he must have preached for hours—and at the back of the picture you can see that he is comfortably perched on a shooting-stick! Splendid!"

"Yes?" said Virginia, who seemed to expect the story to continue.

"That's all. Of course the humour is more in the picture than in the letterpress."

"What was in the letterpress?" said Virginia.

"Well—in fact—er, there wasn't any," answered Tennant, slightly irritated and somewhat dashed.

"Oh," said Virginia.

"We are not amused," murmured Waterlow, *sotto voce*, but not quietly enough for his remark to escape Betty's notice.

"That's Queen Victoria," she said. "I suppose that she's still very much alive here?"

No one seemed anxious to answer this innocent question, but cigarettes, sherry, and general conversation did something to ease the strain, and Tennant began to recover his self-possession. None the less, he tried to steer the conversation away from the guide-book and into safer channels. Winn, however, was not to be warned.

"Tennant thinks, you know," he said, "that the answer to any reasonable question about Oxford can be found in his guide-book, but I——"

"We need not worry about that till later on," Tennant cut in, "there is plenty to see and talk about before you need think of guide-books; besides, the book may not be ready for some little time. But tell me," he went on, boldly carrying the war into the enemy's territory, "what is the first thing you want to see or hear about?"

"Oh, the women's Colleges, of course," replied Betty. "I think it's just wonderful that women here are as important as the men. Now, do tell me all about the women's Colleges, where they are, and which is the best, and do let us go and see them all."

Tennant realised all too clearly that there were, after all, questions to which the guide-book would provide most inadequate answers, but for the moment he was saved from the necessity of a reply by the eager questions of the other two girls.

"I've been studying these last two semesters under Karl Froitzheim at Harvard," said Janet, "for my post-graduate thesis, you know. He's wonderful! Do tell me which of the Oxford professors are working most nearly on his lines. I'd like to have them meet me. It would help me a whole lot when I get back home."

"What part does the student organisation have in governing the College?" demanded Virginia almost in the same breath.

Crushed though he was, Tennant could hardly hear without indignant protest the suggestion that any undergraduate should meddle in the affairs of one of the most respected and conservative of Oxford Colleges, but attacked simultaneously on three fronts he was obliged to be cautious. Even Prendergast admired his effort, when threatened with annihilating defeat, to pluck victory from disaster. Perhaps it flashed through his mind that the greatest test of all generalship was to fight on the retreat, and that time gained might always help to retrieve even the most desperate situation.

So he turned a charming smile on all three ladies, and made a sweeping defensive gesture with his hand.

"A moment, a moment. Of course we'll show you all the women's Colleges. Winn here will love to walk you round them, and I'm sure Waterlow will explain to you just how the students' council watches over our local affairs, and of course I'll get into touch myself with those professors who are best acquainted with Dr. Karl—er—er Portlein. I'm sorry that none of us here works exactly in his special field. But you know all these things are rather—well—part of the working side of Oxford life, and to-day the sun is shining so beautifully—for you ladies no doubt [and he bowed with almost courtly grace]; don't you think we ought to see some of the beauties of Oxford out-of-doors first? Look at some of the gardens and the views that have charmed poets and painters and—er—visitors for centuries—and all that sort of thing?"

Virginia, who was romantic, forgot her student associations at once. "Rather," she said. "Oh, do get a punt and take us all for miles up the river; we've all heard about the river and punts and canoes and parties there."

"And then in the evening let's see the ghosts—there must be hundreds in old buildings like this," cried Betty.

Now if there is one thing that St. Thomas's prides itself upon it is that it has, and will have, no ghost; for a ghost would be out of keeping with the College tradition of dignity and reserve. But considerations of tradition and even of decency could not stop Tennant now, and once more he tried a daring stroke.

"Ghosts!" he said. "Why, yes indeed, the St. Thomas's ghost is world-famous. If you are very fortunate you may well catch a glimpse of it. Why not go now and see whether you will be lucky enough to see it?"

"But whatever's the use of looking for a ghost in the middle of a summer morning?"

"Ah, that's just where the St. Thomas's ghost is peculiar. It is never seen *except* in the middle of the day. Oxford ghosts, you know, cling closely to tradition. At St. John's, for example, Archbishop Laud walks in the College Library but he always seems to be walking on his knees."

"Why ever does he do that?" asked all three girls at once.

"Well, you see, he walks on the old library floor of his days, and since then they've raised the level a foot or two. It's perfectly simple."

"Oh, isn't that sweet! But I don't see why the St. Thomas's ghost walks at midday."

"That's quite simple too." Tennant's confidence—and his inventive genius—were returning to him. "When the calendar was changed, you know, eleven days and all that, in the year—well, in the reign of—er—George II, they got all wrong about times and so on, and well, the ghost thinks it's midnight when in fact it's midday. It's not generally known that they had to make up not eleven days but eleven and a half days. The ghost couldn't be expected to change his habits in that way, and so of course he always comes out just about twelve noon."

Tennant looked at his watch.

"Yes," he went on, "this is just about the best time and the best time of year, too. The ghost appears in the top room of staircase 14—that's the staircase at the end of the far buildings. Now I suggest that Mitton and Pacey take you all up there, and meantime I will 'phone and order a punt for this afternoon and—er—ring up Professor Portlein's friends here, and, in fact, make all the arrangements for the day, and then we can all meet for a drink and lunch in about an hour's time."

Betty's bright eyes had grown brighter and perhaps even suspicious. "But," she said, and then checked herself. "Why, that'll be just lovely."

"But——" stammered Mitton, only to be frowned into silence by Tennant.

"Off you go, Mitton, and Pacey too," he said, "and don't forget the old traditional method. Get the keys and go very quietly into that top room on staircase 14. Sit down by the window and keep quite silent; just watch for the ghost by the fireplace, under the big oak beam where Trefusis hanged himself. And if you don't see him in, say, twenty minutes, you must give it up for to-day. In that case, show the ladies our best views—look at the river and the Berkshire downs and the glimpse of the Colleges in the centre of Oxford, and of course show them the Chapel. And then come back here in good time for lunch."

"I shall be delighted," said Mitton with conviction.

"And so shall I," added Pacey, with rather less enthusiasm. Five minutes later the six seniors were left to themselves in Tennant's room.

"Gentlemen," said Tennant, "for Heaven's sake don't desert me. We are in a jam, but at least we have an hour to improvise some sort of plan of campaign. Somehow we shall wriggle out of it, if we all hang together, but we mustn't waste time. Now, first of all, these women's Colleges—where the deuce are they all? I know Lady Margaret Hall because they built their chapel on the site of the old 'Varsity lawn-tennis courts—a shocking piece of vandalism for they were first-rate courts—but I simply cannot distinguish between St. Hugh's and St. Hilda's. Do any of you know where they are, and will they let us in if we go snooping round them all? Winn, can't you suggest something?"

"I'm not sure," replied Winn. "It's really most perplexing. I feel sure that either St. Hugh's or St. Hilda's was the head hospital in the war because I went to see an old pupil there, but I can't remember if it was in the Banbury or the Iffley Road—you see, I went on a wet day in a taxi and I was reading a book all the time. But I cannot believe," he went on fretfully, "that women are as important as men in Oxford. We have never allowed them in St. Thomas's after the gates are closed for the night; at one time they were not allowed to enter after six in the evening. I think that I shall write a sharp letter to the President and ask him to return to the old rule."

He looked round as though he had disposed of all difficulties.

"In the war," said Tennant bitterly, "there was a lot of anxiety early in 1940 about the possible effects of a bombardment of London, and a high-powered committee was appointed to consider the dangers and suggest remedies. You may, they were told, have ten thousand deaths on your hands overnight. And the committee, so I have been told, after a number of meetings, recommended the appointment of three extra coroners for London. That's what I think of your suggestion, Winn."

"I don't see the relevance of that remark," Winn replied.

"Well, I do," retorted Tennant who had temporarily lost his self-control.

"Kamerad, Kamerad," interposed Waterlow. "Don't quarrel. When the aristos were seated in the tumbril on the way to execution, they never quarrelled with one another—they rather fortified each other with their personal courage. Now, in my experience at St. Thomas's there is an old rule, 'When in doubt, ask the Head Porter'. Surely Martin could tell us all we need to know about these women's Colleges?"

"At last a helpful suggestion," cried Tennant. "Now, Waterlow, it will be your task to obtain from Martin a complete list of all the women's Colleges—*and* a map—*and* you will show the ladies round them all. I will take no denial—your brilliant suggestion shows that you are the man for that job."

"But what about the students' council?" hazarded Prendergast.

"Damn the students' council. I may have sunk pretty low, but nothing will make me descend to such depths as to admit that a students' council is conceivable in St. Thomas's. I just couldn't do that, and I won't. We'll have to stall and put that off till to-morrow. Meanwhile, you, David—yes, you—will invent something about it, and something that will sound plausible. Say that, to increase administrative efficiency, the whole organisation is centred at Balliol, and that to-morrow you will take them round there to meet some of the ring-leaders, or whatever they are called."

"And what," queried Gresham with dangerous quietness, "about this Froitzheim, whom by the way, my dear Tennant, you persist in calling Portlein? Which of your victims is to deal with him? I don't think Miss Janet is going to be put off with a tale about to-morrow and a dubious rendezvous at Balliol."

"Who the devil is Froitzheim? I think he must be a statistical economist," groaned Tennant.

"He sounds to me more like a marine biologist, I don't know why," contributed Waterlow.

"Or a morbid pathologist," suggested Gresham. "What a pity that we sent Pacey away. He would have been sure to know, for this wretched Froitzheim must be a household word in scientific circles. Meantime what can we do to get in touch with his putative disciples and followers here? We don't know where to start."

No one had ever accused Trower of subtlety of mind or of a specially highly developed sense of humour, but he had a certain Blimpish or elephantine faculty of stating the obvious—more to his own enjoyment than to that of his companions. Moreover, he had suffered some not undeserved snubs during the compilation of the guide-book. He struck in, therefore, with unconcealed pleasure at his friends' difficulties.

"To my poor understanding," he observed with ponderous jocularity, "which as you have often pointed out is better adapted to the camp than to the senate, it appears that the great guide-book is not the omniscient volume that its blurb announced it to be. But be that as it may—and I never myself expected that it would stand the first real test—it does occur to me that there is a more immediate problem even than that of discovering the friends of Froitzheim. I mean, of course, the punting problem. Have you realised, Tennant, that you are pledged to propel all these female persons together in a punt for the greater part of the afternoon ? Ha! ha! For miles and miles! Of course for the credit of the College you must do it with plenty of dash and distinction. How do you like that one!"

Tennant emitted a sound which might have been a kind of strangled groan. "I never could keep a punt straight for ten yards," he said.

"Bite on the bullet, my boy, Never say die," urged Trower with relish. "Of course I'm too old to do it myself and my hand may have lost its cunning, but I dare say I can give you a tip or two. Let me see, when I was younger there was a technique known as the St. Hilda's flick—one released one's hand from the punt pole with a graceful and well-timed movement at the end of each stroke. I think it prevented the water from running all the way from the hand to the arm-pit. Most artistic and very much admired. You know, I believe I could teach you the St. Hilda's flick even now if I thought a bit about it. Ha! ha! Why don't you borrow a punt pole, Tennant, and bring it to my Bursary. I'll give you one of your tutorials there. I'll turn you into a 'Cherwell water-lily' like that Bouncer man in *Verdant Green*. And then you know," the Bursar continued, "there is a well-established institution in the States known as a petting-party. I expect the guide-book will tell you just how to organise an Oxford petting-party. Eh, won't it? I only ask for information; they will expect a petting-party, I'm quite sure."

It was beyond the power of the stricken Tennant to rally against these new dangers.

"Don't waste time joking on serious subjects," he groaned. "Won't someone try to help? Can't anyone make some sort of constructive suggestion?"

The silence which ensued was broken by Winn's gentle and scholarly voice.

"As I came in from my walk this morning," he said, "the Head Porter informed me that two of the undergraduates were staying in College for a few nights on their way through Oxford. It does seem to me that they are perhaps more of an age with our American guests and might perhaps be well-fitted to help in their entertainment. Of course, I don't mean," he added hastily, "that you are at all out of touch, Tennant, with modern conditions, but isn't it just possible that some younger men might be helpful to you with the details?"

A drowning man will clutch at a serpent, as the Turkish proverb runs, and a wild and irrational hope surged up in Tennant's mind.

"Who are they?" he said. "Of course they can help—we must get hold of them at once."

"Their names, the Porter said—if I recollect rightly—are Poodle and Ellingham. I don't know them myself."

"But I do," said Waterlow. "Ellingham is a graceless young Philistine from one of our greater public schools, whose spelling makes me doubt the merit of our entrance examination and who seems to be gated for the major portion of every term, and Poodle is an American Rhodes Scholar. They're both second-year. Perhaps neither of them would be automatic choices to write a chapter in an Oxford guide-book—I don't suppose that either of them has heard of the dissolution of the monasteries, or even of St. Scholastica's Day—but in these more present difficulties they might, I should say, be quite useful—and, by Jove, they are walking together across the quad now!"

Tennant rushed to the window. "Call them up at once," he said. "Action, action! Everything is not lost yet."

When, a minute later, Messrs. Poodle and Ellingham were ushered into the room they were not a little surprised to find six of their seniors collected together there. Ellingham in his interviews with authority had usually been on the defensive, but he had learned from long experience that it was sometimes wise to take the initiative.

"I'm sorry, Sir, to come up without a gown, but the Porter told me to come at once. I hope that there is nothing wrong in my being in College in vacation. I'm almost sure that I wrote to the Dean for permission, but of course the letter may have gone astray or been lost in the post." (He did not disclose that the letter had been hastily written and posted ten minutes before when he had realised that his presence in St. Thomas's had been observed.)

"Perfectly, perfectly—don't worry yourself in the least," replied Tennant. "At St. Thomas's we always like to see our *alumni* and our undergraduates here at any time. I like to feel that your spiritual home is also your material home, even in vacation. But tell me, Mr. Ellingham, do you know anything of the women's Colleges?"

Uncertain whether *alumni* was a term of reproach or not, Ellingham tried cautiously to adjust himself to the new position. Apparently he was not 'on the mat', but it might still be best to be wary.

"Well, Sir," he said, "of course I do; it wouldn't be possible to be a year at Oxford and not know them all, would it?"

"No—er—I suppose not," said Tennant. "But I mean do you know where they all are, and all about them, and what studies they pursue, and which of them has the best buildings and so forth?"

"Certainly," said Ellingham with growing confidence. "Of course everyone knows that by far the nicest girls are at——"

"No, no, no, spare us those guilty secrets," cried Tennant. "Do you know anything about a students' council?"

Winn interrupted before an answer could be given to Tennant's question.

"Please don't ask him about that. I try to move with the times and to adjust myself to modern conditions, but he might say that he was President of it or something like that, and I really don't think that I could bear to know that there was such an institution in St. Thomas's itself. Could you not rather ask Mr. Poodle if he has heard of Professor Froitzheim?"

Everyone turned to the Rhodes Scholar. Was it possible that by some fantastic stroke of good fortune he would be able to provide a clue to that mystery?

"Karl Froitzheim?" said Poodle, who seemed a little unnerved by the unexpected reference to himself. "Karl Froitzheim, why, yes, I know what everyone else in England and the States knows about him; I know all that, of course, but not more than that."

Everyone waited for him to continue, but he appeared to think that he had said enough.

Prendergast tried to encourage him.

"Yes, quite, quite, but how, for example, would you define what everyone on both sides of the Atlantic knows?"

"Well," said Poodle, "I suppose I ought to have said what every educated person knows about him—yes, that would have been a more accurate definition."

It was a little tantalising for six Fellows of St. Thomas's to be told that the precious secret was known to all educated persons in two continents and yet to be unable to find out what it was.

Trower, with soldierly directness, launched a frontal attack.

"How would you define his exact, his special, line of study?" he asked.

"That's rather a technical question," said Poodle, and relapsed into silence.

There was almost a pleading note in Trower's voice as he made another effort.

"Surely you could define it, though, in quite general terms?"

"I don't think I could," said the cautious Poodle. "Of course he's the greatest living authority on pedagogics and theories of education, but then everyone connected with a University or even faintly interested in education must know that. Why, Dr. Dimley at Magdalen lectures on him three days a week, and of course all the dons at the Department of Education talk about him and his theories day and night, but I really don't think I could define his special line of investigation."

A sigh of relief seemed to come from six of his listeners at the same moment, and Tennant could not restrain his enthusiasm.

"Mr. Poodle," he said, "you are come straight from Heaven."

"Oh no, Sir, I'm from Alabama!"

"Don't contradict your seniors, Poodle. You may have come via Alabama perhaps, but indubitably you are sent from Heaven."

"Can either of you handle a punt?" interjected Waterlow.

Ellingham had by this time satisfied himself that no misdeed of the past was being held against him, and his curiosity was aroused.

"I can manage a punt as well as the next man, and, in fact, I've got a punt belonging to me on the river; but could you tell me, Sir, what it's all about?"

Tennant rose to his feet to reply. "Gentlemen," he said, "we have no wish to burden you with idle questions. It so happens that

266

something in the nature of a crisis has coincided with your return to the College, and that, in a very real sense, the honour of St. Thomas's is at stake. Three young ladies have been sent here by one of our most distinguished old members, and we are all concerned to show them during the next day or two all that is best and most characteristic of Oxford. They come, if I may put it so, from Mr. Poodle's country, where they have been most hospitable to travelling Englishmen, and the most elementary courtesy demands that we should do all that we can for them on this side. But—not to put too fine a point on it—we are of opinion that we are perhaps a little elderly to entertain and amuse them, and we thought, maybe, that some younger society for part of the time might possibly increase the pleasure of their visit. You might, perhaps, take them for a punting excursion on the river, to which they appear partial, or even to some dance or dinner or mild celebration on one of the evenings that they are here. Of course my colleagues and myself will do the major part of the work—if such a pleasurable task can be so described—but we thought that, for the credit of the College, you might feel disposed to add your small contribution to our efforts."

Ellingham's face would not have disgraced a poker player from Mr. Poodle's country, and Tennant had a sudden fear that all his happy anticipations might collapse, so he hurried on. "I need hardly say that in a crisis of this kind no expense must be spared, and naturally all charges of every kind will be borne by the College. It would be only right, I think, to do things (if I may lapse into the vernacular) on a rather lavish scale."

Ellingham's face had gradually relaxed during this speech, and he was not a man to miss any opportunity.

"I shall be most happy," he said, "to do any little thing in my power to assist. Is the crisis so great that it might run to champagne?"

Tennant made his most sweeping gesture. "Where the reputation of the College is concerned, no cheeseparing is to be thought of. Yes, this might well be considered as a champagne crisis. I will consult the College Butler. But, Poodle, you will assist also?"

"Are the young ladies in question those that I saw going across the quad with Mr. Mitton just now?" asked the cautious Poodle.

"They are."

"Then certainly, one hundred per cent," declared Poodle with decision.

"Excellent. Now can either of you make any suggestions to improve on our plans? Lunches and dinners and a punting party and some sort of celebration in the evenings, and seeing all the sights of Oxford, the Colleges, and the women's Colleges and the gardens and everything. We want them, you know, to absorb the spirit of Oxford, and to see all that is best and most permanent here, so that they carry away something of value with them when they go. Can either of you suggest any additions to fill in the programme?"

"They say there is a first-class picture at the Super this week," said Ellingham. "We might take them to that—or we could all dance somewhere."

"I could mix a good Mint Julep one evening," said Poodle, "if I had the Bourbon."

When Tennant surrendered he surrendered, as he did everything else, wholeheartedly. "By all means take them to the cinema," he said, "even if it curtails some of our talks about Oxford antiquities. And a Mint Julep seems to be essential. If I rightly understand Bourbon to mean corn whisky, you shall have it, if the Butler has to scour every county between Thames and Trent. But first of all, we must introduce you to the ladies. Both of you must come to lunch and meet them to arrange our plans— in the Senior Common Room about one o'clock. Oh, and now I think of it, it seems to me that I have perhaps ordered wines more suitable to elderly palates than to those of our guests and yourselves. Would you be kind enough to go to the Butler in the Senior Common Room and order all the drinks you think most suitable for a warm day instead of the wines I had told him to have ready. I mean cocktails and cups and all that kind of thing. Anything that you think conducive to easy conversation and—er—general hilarity. Thank you both very much—the College is in your debt already."

A general easing of tension followed the departure of the undergraduates. Winn allowed himself to relax in his armchair, Gresham fanned himself with *The Times* and Trower helped himself to a stiff whisky and soda, whilst Tennant filled the sherry glasses of the others.

"I really think," he said, "that we are out of the wood now."

"Except, perhaps, for the students' council," said Prendergast.

"If those words are mentioned again, "replied Tennant savagely, "we must take a high hand. Dash it all, if half a dozen of us can't talk down one weak woman we deserve to lose our Fellowships, and in any case——"

At that moment, however, the rasping cough of Martin was heard and another knock came on the door.

"Sir John Boomer to see you, Sir," said the Porter. The large and sanguine face of the Baronet was wreathed in smiles as he entered the room.

"Hullo, everyone," he said. "How are you all, and how is St. Thomas's? Why, Tennant, you look as though you'd just left your own funeral!"

"I thought you were in South Africa," Tennant stuttered.

"Ha! ha! Well, I did say I was going there, but to tell the truth I couldn't resist coming along to see how my little joke would pan out. I always think that you dons want stirring up now and then. A little female society is good for all of you. But no one has offered me a glass of sherry yet."

Tennant, who was speechless, handed him a glass.

"Thank you. I'll drink to celebrate the success of my hoax. Splendid. It's all gone according to Cocker. I enjoy a good practical joke every now and then. Now, tell me what sort of impression did my Americans make on you? Come on, Winn, what did you think of them?"

Winn replied somewhat stiffly. "In my sheltered life," he said, "I have not been exposed—or rather, I should say, I have seldom had the great good fortune to be brought much into contact with society of this kind."

Sir John, however, had already turned to Gresham.

"I've no doubt that you soon decided which of them was your fancy—eh, Gresham? Which of them did you think the most fetching?"

Gresham flinched, as he often did when Sir John's vulgarity of speech touched him on the raw, but he tried to reply courteously.

"I thought them all charming," he replied, "but in my wildest moments I have never cast myself for the part of Paris."

It was characteristic of Sir John Boomer that he seldom listened with any care to the answers to his own questions.

"By gad, Gresham, you're going the pace," he exclaimed. "You've known my young friends for about half an hour and you're talking of taking them off to Paris! 'Pon my soul——"

"I alluded to a person of that name but of earlier date," interrupted Gresham. "I can assure you——"

"Well, well," Sir John went on, patting him upon an unwilling shoulder, "we'll say no more about that, but let's set out to enjoy ourselves for the next few days." He beamed on the assembled company. "But what have you done with the ladies?"

"Did your American friends know about your little joke?" asked Prendergast in icy tones.

"Betty did. She's the clever one. She'd have guessed even if I hadn't told her. Got a sense of humour, too. Why, I thought at one time of making her Lady Boomer—I did, really. She knew all about it. I thought that one of you might possibly have guessed, too, but there again I thought you wouldn't. I've always said that you dons haven't much sense of humour—that's why I like to come and cheer you up now and then. But don't let's bother about that now. I've laid on plenty of entertainment for the next three days and Callender has fixed some slap-up lunches and dinners for us. You're all invited and we'll enjoy ourselves properly. I'll guarantee that we'll have some fun talking about my leg-pull, and how I took you all in, at dinner to-night."

With immense satisfaction Sir John drained his glass and refilled it.

"Am I to understand," asked Winn almost tearfully, "that Callender knew about your visit?"

"Of course he did; he's a most reliable man and most discreet. Besides, I couldn't fix all the parties for my guests without his help."

"And he has listened to us for a week, and watched us toiling at this wretched guide-book without saying a word! He might have given us some warning," groaned Prendergast.

"Of course he didn't say a word," replied Sir John. "I told him not to, and he's the soul of discretion. You are lucky to have such a man here. But what's this guide-book you spoke of?"

"No," said Tennant. "The guide-book which David mentioned by inadvertence is another matter altogether, and does not really fit at all into the framework of a 'a little joke'. Some other time, perhaps——"

"Very well," said Boomer. "I'm not inquisitive. But oughtn't we to be finding the ladies and thinking about our lunch? I hope Callender has lived up to his reputation with that lunch."

The last humiliation was reserved for Tennant. "I must tell you," he said, "that, not knowing that you would be our host at lunch, I have asked two undergraduates to join us. We thought that they would be agreeable company for the ladies."

"Oh, that's all right," said Sir John. "I don't mind how many guests I have—the more the merrier."

"Thank you, but—well, I suggest that we need not tell them about your—your—very ingenious piece of deception. I feel that it would not be altogether good for College discipline if the undergraduates knew how—er—skilfully you had taken us all in."

Sir John Boomer roared with laughter.

"They won't be told by me, if that's your wish," he replied. "But unless undergraduates have changed very much since my day, there isn't much they won't have ferreted out about it by lunch time at latest. That's the worst of you dons," he added, putting salt in the wound, "you don't know the first thing about the undergraduates—or what goes on in the world to-day." (He dug Winn playfully in the ribs, and Winn shuddered involuntarily.) "You're all fossilised in the past. Why don't you cultivate a real College spirit, and get everyone at St. Thomas's to know each other? I shall have to come here more often and bring you all together."

Waterlow was a sensitive man, and the thought of a couple of days listening to Sir John's accounts of his little joke and to homilies on the duties of dons appalled him.

"It has been a pleasure, Sir John, to see you unexpectedly like this," he said in his best Foreign Office manner. "I'm only distressed that we did not know earlier that you would be here. Only an hour ago I wired to accept an invitation to stay in Devonshire, [Prendergast gave him an appealing glance]—ah, yes, for David Prendergast and myself to stay for a day or two in Devonshire, and I fear that we must start our drive immediately after luncheon. I am profoundly disappointed, but *noblesse oblige*, as no one will know better than yourself."

"That's a pity," Sir John replied. "But it can't be helped. We'll have lunch as soon as possible—but where are the girls?"

"I think they are waiting for a ghost and wondering why

Trefusis hanged himself, though I can imagine plenty of good reasons for that," replied Tennant gloomily.

At that moment, however, peals of laughter, not all feminine, were heard on the stairs.

"Did you see the ghost?" asked Tennant, with a rather pathetic effort to maintain his shattered defences.

"Oh yes!" said Betty, with a gurgle of laughter. "Poor Mr. Trefusis!"

It was very late on the Wednesday night, but Winn, Gresham, and Tennant lingered in the Common Room.

"I always drink too much when Sir John dines here," said Winn irritably. "I wish to be charitable, but I cannot listen to him patiently; he is, I find, intolerably long-winded, and he always breaks in, most rudely, when others are speaking. Besides, the aroma of his cigars clings to the curtains in a way which I find most distasteful. And when I drink more than two glasses my night's rest is entirely spoiled. It is all most provoking."

"And I," said Tennant, savagely, "am quite unable to drink enough when he is there. Intoxication is the only remedy, and that seems to be out of my reach. And when I think of all this wasted effort! I still maintain that for a reasonable—and male—public the guide-book would have been a useful book. It would have contained the essence of Oxford—I'm sure it would have—but how could we interpret Oxford to young women who are interested in cocktails and cinemas and punting and pedagogics and students' councils—and mint juleps and abominations like that? Well, I've had my lesson, I shall never write the guide-book now, and my long, lovely, leisured book on Oxford will never be written either. And to think that I once thought that I could tell the secret of Oxford to this generation! If Mitton were here he would rightly call it a generation of vipers."

"Would he not be more likely to favour you with some not

inconsiderable part of his sermon on humility, to which I have listened many times during the last fifteen years?" said Winn. "Dear me, it is a curious thing that when I drink more than I should my brain seems to grow much clearer, though I am told that the experience of others would lead me to expect the opposite. Do not you think, my dear Tennant, that you are exaggerating the troubles and even the humiliations of to-day?"

Gresham smiled. "Yes," he said. "I also think that you are taking it too hardly. Are you quite sure that we haven't gone near to penetrating the secret of Oxford, after all?"

"What do you mean?" asked Tennant. "Pray, to use your own phrase, be explicit."

"My meaning is this. As we have discussed Oxford and its different aspects, we have always tended to return to our own early days. Each of us sees it as it was when he was young, each of us thinks that his own age was by much the best, each of us thinks that his successors ought to enjoy the things which he enjoyed and to admire what he admired. But why should they? Isn't it right that every generation should live its own life and worship its own gods?

> The world's great age begins anew,
> The golden years return.

The great age for us was the age of our youth, but it seems to me that every October, when the freshmen arrive, the great age dawns for them and the golden years begin. We're here to help them if we can, not to impose our standards and our views and our rules of conduct upon them. Your famous secret cannot be told because for each individual it is a different secret—and each must find it for himself. Do I make myself clear?"

Winn had, without any realisation of what he was doing, helped himself to another glass of wine, and he now gave an almost senile chuckle. "When I was young," he said, "we used to be warned not to try to teach our grandparents—let me see, what was the phrase—ah yes, I remember, it was a very rude expression —to suck eggs. It appears to me, Gresham, that you think that we should be equally cautious in our dealings with our grandchildren. An interesting speculation."

He drained his glass, and seemed to be trying to remember what he had in mind. Then with a flash of the old fire he turned to Tennant.

"That young man Pacey made the outrageous suggestion that we should install fluorescent lighting in this room," he said. "I trust, Tennant, that you will exert your influence to prevent an atrocity of that kind. Change in Oxford, in my experience, is almost always for the worse."

NOTES

1. p. 15. Four of the eight diners appeared as characters in *An Oxford Tragedy* (1933). Time has dealt not unkindly with three of them—Winn, Trower, and Prendergast, but I confess to a feeling of disappointment when I consider how Mitton has developed—or failed to develop—with the years. It might have been expected that the war would have broadened his outlook and enlarged his sympathies; instead, he seems to have become obtuse, rather self-satisfied and singularly blind to the ideas of other men. Winn tries to be charitable towards him, but cannot altogether disguise from me his regrets that St. Thomas's should be saddled with a Chaplain who cannot rank very high in reputation among College Chaplains. My own feeling is that he has become less and less like the normal College Chaplain, but then, as Mitton himself would certainly say, "it takes all sorts to make a world".

2. p. 52. It is curious that Winn appears to be unfamiliar with the published views of Sir Charles Firth on this subject—especially his *Modern History in Oxford 1841–1918*.

3. p. 66. Some of Tennant's notes which have been preserved indicate that at this point the discussion was interrupted whilst Prendergast delivered an impassioned defence of lawyers; an extract from these notes follows. (Tennant has written in pencil in the margin "Not to be used unless Aristotle is a lawyer".) "I think that I have established my point that every man, who values happiness, should guide his life and his relations with other men by the advice of his lawyer. Gentlemen's agreements, casual oral arrangements, hastily worded private letters are like short cuts in an unfamiliar country which almost invariably cause waste of time, exhaustion, and misfortune. Stick rather to the high road

of the law! Remember, too, that accurate and precise definition prevents the majority of human misunderstandings and troubles. The lawyer is, indeed, mankind's best friend, and no calling or profession can compare in value with the law. Science, you say, Pacey, because it advances civilisation, but how many of your scientific inventions have only increased the potentialities of war and destruction? If all the world accepted a rule of law there would be no more war. Medicine? Again No! I grant that the physician or the surgeon can do much to alleviate human suffering, but many ills are beyond their skill, and cannot be prevented or cured by human agency. The lawyer, on the other hand, can and does resolve the troubles of his client—in business, in public affairs, in private life. All difficulties encountered in these spheres are man-made and therefore susceptible of a remedy. The Church? No, no, Mitton! Study the history of your country and you will be compelled to admit that the Church has too often been a reactionary force, resisting progress, nourishing privilege, even at times sunk in obscurantism—whilst lawyers have been in the forefront of every worthy and progressive cause. I repeat that the lawyer is mankind's best friend, but permit me to develop my argument in greater detail." At this point Tennant's notes come to an abrupt end.

4. p. 95. Winn's celebrated essay on historical truth was first read to a St. Thomas's literary society in 1903. Since then it has been often revised and enlarged but not published. The author feels that publication should be postponed until his college history is completed. Meantime the development of the conception of guide-book truth creates difficulties. Winn had arrived at an understanding of the difference between those things which were true historically and those true only in a Pickwickian sense; he feels less secure in discussing those things which are true in a guide-book sense. Gresham and Tennant maintain that guide-book truth bears the same relation to historical truth as an impressionist portrait does to a Victorian likeness. They go so far as to maintain that the former gives the essential truth which is concealed by the latter.

5. p. 97. It is possible, but not certain, that the staircase system

developed from these Benedictine buildings. Be that as it may, it is surely arguable that the essential difference between a school and a University is that the one has rooms opening on to corridors—the other rooms placed on a staircase. The corridor, for any sensitive person, betokens the extinction of studious habits. An interesting architectural attempt to combine the corridor and staircase system may be seen in the New Buildings at Worcester.

6. p. 100. Burgon's poem on Worcester is printed in *Arms of the Colleges of Oxford* by Shaw and Burgon, but Gresham does the poem scant justice. It may be sentimental but it is singularly beautiful in phrasing and feeling—and it is set down with economy of words. I am tempted to quote it *in extenso*, but the function of a guide-book is to stimulate the reader to further researches rather than to exhaust a subject.

7. p. 126. Blücher to Gneisenau, after his return from England, 20 July, 1814. "*Was dass Trinken in Engelandt betrifft: so hatte ich grosse angst, aber man forcirte mich nicht, und ich hatte gleich Declarirt dass ich kein andern wein wie Bordou trinke und dabei bin ich auch geblieben. So hallte ich es mit die Herrn auss.*"

8. p. 129. "*Il y a deux cents cinquante chambres où quelqu'un confesse la médecine, deux cents cinquante lits où un corps étendu témoigne que la vie a un sens, et grâce à moi un sens médical. . . . Songez que, pour tout ce monde leur premier office est de rappeler mes prescriptions; qu'elles sont la voix de mes ordonnances. Songez que, dans quelques instants, il va sonner dix heures, que pour tous mes malades, dix heures, c'est la deuxième prise de température rectale, et que, dans quelques instants, deux cent cinquante thermomètres vont pénétrer à la fois . . .*"

NOTES

9. p. 147. It is related that complaints were made to one Proctor because an undergraduate had been observed bathing naked late one summer evening from his College barge. The undergraduate was fined 5/- for bathing after dark without cap and gown.

10. p. 153. The first of the three parts of *Verdant Green*, 1853-4-7, appeared as a shilling railway novel. This most popular of University stories, the adventures of an Oxford Freshman, was written by Edward Bradley, a graduate of University College, Durham, who used the names of Cuthbert and Bede, the patron saints of Durham. The first part was written for the illustrations which had been intended for *Punch*. Twenty-five of them appeared in two of the Supplements of the *Illustrated London News* in Dec.-Jan. ,1851-2. More blocks had been prepared, but the editor stopped the Supplements. So Bradley wrote the book and with difficulty got it printed. "It will never pay the expenses," said the publisher. In 1883 Bradley said the electrotypes were much worn by some 170,000 copies being printed. In an article in *The American Oxonian*, 1933, which reprints much of a long account by Bradley of the history of *Verdant Green* (he started as *Verdant Vivid*) the late Mr. Carroll A. Wilson estimated that more than 250,000 copies had been sold. Bradley only got £350 and until he was "safe in a living" declined to write anything of "a similar nature"—"My *Verdant Green* has already been an obstacle to me in my clerical profession". He got the living but lost the art of writing things of a similar nature.

11. p. 168. The reputation of the Head of a House to whom Waterlow refers was well deserved, for it was seldom that he could not match, from his personal experience, the feats and triumphs of any competitor. It was currently believed (by the credulous) that he had dived from greater heights, shot more birds in the air at the same time, done more holes in one, and broken more sporting records than any living person. "Chess?" he said on one occasion. "No, I am not a great chess-player for I have not devoted time to the study of it—but I enjoy

a game. Once crossing the Atlantic the champion of the world, who happened to be on board, was anxious for a game after dinner, and I volunteered to play with him. I took white. I moved, he moved, I moved, he moved, I moved, he moved; fool's mate, I said. He was never so surprised in his life. But, of course, I don't play the game seriously."

12. p. 172. I am at loss to understand how Gresham obtained this note, for it appears to be a quotation from R. F. Harrod's life of John Maynard Keynes. This book was not published till 1951, yet Gresham seems able to quote from it two years before it was written. Like Winn, I own that I am perplexed.

13. p. 190. Christopher Wordsworth, *Social Life at the English Universities in the Eighteenth Century* (1874), and *Scholæ Academicæ— Studies at the English Universities in the Eighteenth Century* (1877).

14. p. 192. This extract is part of a long Latin letter written by Marshall to John Postlethwayt, D.D., High Master of St. Paul's.

15. p. 192. James Hurdis (1763–1801) was elected Professor of Poetry in 1793. In the *D.N.B.* he receives little credit either for his *Vindication* or for his poetry. The following lines, from *The Favorite Village,* suggest, however, that he had a true appreciation of nature and a vivid power of description.

> *Ten thousand thousand of rich furze, erewhile*
> *By the fast fleecy nibbler neatly trimmed,*
> *And decorated now in robe superb,*
> *Wrapping its branches in a blaze of gold*
> *As if the Deity himself were there.*

16. p. 197. Mitton's observation is not original. In *Our Memories* (Daniel, Oxford, 1893) occurs this paragraph:

"Another of *Mo Griffith's* special friends was Dr. *Macbride*, the Principal of Magdalen Hall. The two were nearly contemporaries, and, when both of them had passed the age of eighty, were in the habit of taking their mild 'constitutional' together two or three days a week. On one occasion *Mo* remarked to his friend—'There's one change in Oxford, *Macbride*, that I can't at all make out. Don't you remember, when we were young, there used to be a number of queer old fellows among the Dons—*Quizzes* we used to call them—curious old chaps it made one laugh to see. Now I don't see any such fellows about.' 'Perhaps,' replied the more sagacious Principal, 'you and I, Mr. *Griffith*, may seem to the young men of to-day the sort of persons of whom you speak.' '*You and I!* impossible, impossible!' And the subject was not pursued any further."

17. p. 211. Cannister belonged to a period which believed in the health-giving properties of the rowing breakfast. Even as late as Gresham's day breakfast for the Eight would begin with stewed fruit and porridge, followed by fried fish, a couple of eggs, and a large steak. Marmalade and fresh fruit would complete the gargantuan meal. Damon Runyon's triumphant winner of the eating contest might well have feared a challenge from a member of the St. Thomas's Eight at the beginning of the century.

18. p. 212. What entitles a man to be called conscientious? Dr. Bloomfield, Bishop of Chester, reproved a rector for drunkenness, and received the reply, in an injured manner, that the rector was never drunk on duty. (J. L. and B. Hammond, *The Village Labourer, 1760–1832*.)

19. p. 224. The discussion on the College system seems to be based

on two articles, one written by Dr. C. K. Allen in the University Handbook—the other, entitled *The Oxford College System and its Preservation*, by the late W. T. S. Stallybrass, published in the *American Oxonian*, January 1948.

20. p. 235. Gresham tells me that he would have wished to talk at greater length of the personal relations of the tutor and his pupils had Tennant permitted. He therefore asks me to add this note of his personal reminiscence of tutors. "When I was first summoned to my tutor at the beginning of a cold and foggy Michaelmas term, I was told to go to his house—which was not far from the College—at seven-thirty in the morning. Unwillingly I obeyed. 'Can you see my pencil on my desk?' were my tutor's first words. 'I have been looking for it all the morning.' From that remark I learned to respect tutors—even though I came to know later that I was not the only pupil to whom this question had been addressed! I think that tutors in the past were apt to be more downright than those of to-day. Under one of my old essays (which was, I admit, a pompous and wordy production) is written in the bold hand of my tutor: 'Too much scaffolding left up.' I cannot recall that any other criticism was made or expected. It was good advice, and I hope I have profited from it. 'To call that nonsense would be paying it a compliment. Good morning'—was all the satisfaction which a contemporary of mine received after reading a not very good essay to his tutor. Perhaps the majesty of the tutor is best illustrated by the tale of Buchanan—'the elegant and immortal historian' as he is described—who was tutor to King James I. The story will be found in the first volume of Disraeli's *Curiosities of Literature*."

21. p. 249. Sir E. Barker in *The Times*, May 7, 1949.